Discount Coupon

AMERICAN GIRL

Bearer is entitled to 24 *issues of* **American Girl** (ages 11-17)

regularly by subscription $7.00

by single copy $9.60

K6 04

OUR PRICE **ONLY $4.44**

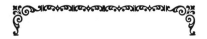

Charming You

Charming You

MARJORIE FROST

ZONDERVAN PUBLISHING HOUSE
GRAND RAPIDS, MICHIGAN

In

loving memory

of my

MOTHER

and

MRS. KATE LANGWORTHY WOODWORTH

my college benefactress
who requested anonymity
during her lifetime

Contents

Charming You

Charming You

You are charming!

I'm convinced of it . . . because I have yet to meet a lady or girl devoid of charm. Granted, no one was ever born with her charm in full bloom. With the proverbial "silver spoon in her mouth," yes. But instinctively knowing and observing the many feminine niceties?

This does not come, as a package deal, with a famous family name or a prestige address. The details of charm must, in each case, be acquired. They must be learned.

This feminine service, formerly rendered by finishing schools to a select clientele, is now being performed by charm schools, mushrooming up all over the country. People are signing up for these courses in modeling schools, adult evening courses, department stores, Y.W.C.A.'s, clubs, church-oriented organizations and in private homes. Courses are given to women in the armed forces and in airline stewardess schools.

Charm schools are geared to *all* members of the fairer sex, because charm and femininity are without knowledge of age barriers and class distinctions.

We heard one grandmother say that learning to walk without having her elbows protrude was in itself worth the price of the course to her. Another class had a charming mother participate right along with her daughters and their young friends.

As we acquire more self-assurance, we need less time to think of ourselves and so can turn our attention more whole-heartedly to *others*. Also, self-confidence breeds happiness, and happiness in turn opens doors to productivity and rich experiences.

Appreciating the importance of current charm schools, but sensing their need for a more basic foundation and for an added dimension, I was challenged to work out a course to meet this need. Thus *Charming You* was conceived.

The contents of *Charming You* were gleaned from a happy, patchwork-quilt background: childhood in the parsonage; work in a girls' social service department; teaching biology, health and English in public and Christian high schools; teaching in camps and Sunday schools; some graduate work in dramatics; play producing and acting; study in the business and professional women's course at an eastern modeling school and a recent refresher course in the midwest, followed by the sponsoring of a few charm classes in private homes and church-affiliated groups.

In mulling over this list of unrelated teachings and experiences, I'm aware that it is their very diversification which has made *Charming You* possible. Each experience made its own unique contribution.

I have attempted to cull out extraneous material and to offer only those features qualified to enhance one's poise and self-confidence in the ordinary, everyday situations.

Thanks to my friends, neighbors and family, there was no scarcity of models for all the ideas. I only wish I could have included them all. Reminiscing about these different people, some of whom I haven't seen for years, has been one of the most pleasant side-effects of this work.

You may wish that some subjects had been treated in more detail, others in less. Also, you may not fully agree with some of the ideas expressed — perhaps we were taught differently, or our varied observations led to different conclusions.

The ideas written here have all been tested and modifications and additions have been made.

The first class I sponsored was taught by a select group of charming young mothers, each one a living model. But not every community or group is fortunate enough to claim Jacqueline Bell, Jean Bolinder, Carolyn Cartwright, Joanne Hollatz, and Fran Schwaber as part of its natural resources. So, I have chosen to write this, not as a teacher's guide (though it could be that), but as a personal book for *you.*

You will find that all of the suggestions for feminine charm and self-assurance are specific — not like the old-fashioned butter-the-size-of-an-egg-type recipe. You will have no difficulty following these simple, concise instructions to a lovelier you.

But certainly you are not just so many robots, to "click, clack, click" to the count of "1 . . . 2 . . . 3." The basic steps of *Charming You* can furnish only the outline to a beautiful picture. You will each be adding your own differences and personality to individualize your particular "picture," because each of you is a unique, one-of-a-kind individual!

You will be studying about YOU, the *visible* you, and the

inner *real* you, and intertwining with these thoughts will
be substantiating quotes from the Author of your life.
This Author, you will recall, was the proud Father of His
Son, who "increased in wisdom, in stature, in favor with
God and (in favor with) man!"

The fact that social favor is important in His sight,
would seem to make it all the more imperative that we
cherish and nourish this side of our lives, too.

In some circles, the subject of social graces is unfortun-
ately often completely ignored, or squeezed into a brief
discussion which is couched in unsatisfactory generalities.

◦◦◦

After I had given quite a long talk about politeness and
personal cleanliness to my daughters (then only four and
six years old), the younger one said, "Could you please
write that out for me?"

I just stared at her!

Margo couldn't even read. Besides, she had appeared
bored all during the talk.

"I mean — what you just said," she explained. "I wish
you'd write it all out. Then, when I get to be a mother,
I can read it all to my girls."

◦◦◦

"Why classes just for teenagers?" queried some ladies.
"What about us mothers? We're the ones who'd appreciate
some new ideas."

◦◦◦

These two incidents, plus the following excerpt from a
letter, comprised a triple prod for *Charming You.*

"If you have been only dreaming about the writing you
would like to do someday, I challenge you to stop putting
it off! The tempo of these times will not tolerate dawdling.

Somebody is waiting to read what *you* have to say." (In a form letter from Dr. Melvin E. Lorentzen, Assistant Professor of English, Wheaton College, Wheaton, Illinois)

I deeply appreciate the confidence expressed by the different individuals who have encouraged me all along the way and for those special few who have faithfully "remembered" this project.

For their interest and professional support, I wish to express my gratitude to Dr. Kenneth Taylor, Dr. Mary LeBar, Dr. and Mrs. Gordon Jaeck, and Margaret Deschauer Johnson.

My special thanks go to Rosalinda Karolek and Mary Bolen for their reading of parts of the manuscript, and to Dorothea Jaeck and Joanne Hollatz for their critical reading of the galley proofs, and to all four ladies for their beneficial suggestions.

I deeply appreciate the pleasant and significant help of Mary Ruth Howes, Assistant Book Editor of Zondervan Publishing House.

The individuals and companies to whom I wrote for quote permissions were extremely prompt and gracious in complying. Special care has been given to secure all necessary permissions. If, in spite of this, any were overlooked, I sincerely apologize. Any such oversight would be corrected before the second printing.

And finally, my warmest thanks go to my cooperative and long-suffering family.

And so, as a teacher of teenagers, a mother of this same lovable, unpredictable age, and the daughter of a precious lady (now with the Author of her inner beauty), I write this book with *you* in mind.

Thoughtfully yours,

Marjorie Frost

1

Let's Get Acquainted

This business of being self-appointed judges as to what is or is not beautiful in others has always been with us and shows no signs of a quick demise. People do observe and do judge one another's appearance, though this might well be done unconsciously.

Tell me, what is the first thing that *you* notice about someone to whom you are being introduced?

"It varies with the individual," you answer.

Yes, it could be the sheen of her hair, the mod look, or her smiling eyes. True, but don't these answers boil down to one general term — *appearance?* How one looks?

Some people, like my friend Dorothy, have the faculty to recall with almost photographic accuracy a person's features and the complete outfit she was wearing. Many of us remember only the general impression (neat, fault-lessly groomed, tacky, coordinated colors). But everyone remembers *something* about the way others look.

The old saying that man looks on the outward appear-

ance but that God looks on the heart could be passed off
as an innocuous truism heard from early childhood; *or*
this thought could well cause one to do a double-take...
reach for one's Bible... and thoughtfully read I Samuel
16:7:

> The Lord seeth not as man seeth;
>   for man looketh on the outward appearance,
> but the Lord looketh on the heart.

This is saying incisively to me... "You, Marjorie, are
open to *double* scrutiny — from *people* and from *God.*
People are looking at you!"

"People?"

"Yes, the other members of your family and..."

"Oh, but they love me," I interrupt. "And a head full
of curlers or a pair of scuffed-up house slippers is not
going to prompt a house meeting to discuss exchanging
me for another model," I might add flippantly.

"But," the Voice continues, "your neighbors and friends,
the bank teller, the beautician, the other supermarket
shoppers, the salesladies. *People*... people everywhere are
looking at you and consciously or otherwise are judging
the way you look.

"This superficial appraisal of your outward appearance
is a daily fact," the Voice reiterates. "And equally factual
is the constant in-depth scrutiny of your heart, *the real
you,* by the One who originally fashioned you and who,
more than anyone else, is vitally interested in you as a
person."

And so, in a matter of a few meditative moments, this
commonplace verse can metamorphize into a two-edged
sword... a double-barreled gun.

People are watching me. God is watching me. I am
important!

You are being observed. People are watching you, the way you *look*, the way you *act*, and the way you *talk*; God is watching you, the *real you*, the unvarnished, down-deep you. You are important! !

Think of all the people during Christ's life here who looked at Him! Yet all of His eighteen busy years between the time He was twelve and thirty years of age were compressed into one simple sentence:

> Jesus increased in wisdom and stature,
> and in favor with God and man (Luke 2:52).

Here we have another verse that bears meditation.

Jesus increased in:

wisdom (intellectually)
> stature (physically)
>> favor with God (spiritually)
>>> favor with man (socially).

If God the Father thought it was important for His Son to increase in *each* of these specific areas, important enough to have it recorded in His written Word, then who are we to feel ourselves exempt from growth in any *one* of these areas?

Intellectual Growth

The fact that you have started reading another book shows your interest in this area of development.

You girls are being directed in your intellectual growth by your parents, school teachers, Sunday school teachers and Youth Directors.

We ladies (wives, mothers, grandmothers, career ladies) have a wealth of material at our disposal . . . books, magazines, programs, travel, discussion groups and adult education offerings.

Intellectual growth is too exciting to be limited to those of school age.

My mother-in-law doesn't just sit on her Florida rocking chair dreaming of her upstate New York school-
teaching years. Work in her vegetable and flower gardens
and oil painting occupy many hours. Dropping in on
Grandma Frost means you're in for a game of Scrabble,
and don't be surprised if she wins! Last spring she taught
our daughters to crochet and they taught her how to knit.
She studies courses so that she, in turn, can teach them to
the ladies' group of her church. Anyone of lesser mettle
would fill her hours complaining (or bragging) about her
poor health. Within the last eight years she has been tapped
262 times for excess fluid because of cirrhosis of the liver.
This operation is required every twelve days now. Grandma
must have come from good pioneer stock.

Last week a Friends of the Library group sat charmed
listening to a modest little lady describe her initiation into
the writing field. She had never taken any courses in writing. She had no assurance that she could write. But one
evening after work, she sat down at her typewriter.

Four years later, at the insistence of her sister, she mailed
her manuscript to a publisher, expecting a rejection slip
within the next six months. Instead, she received an accep-
tance within six weeks. And so *April Snow* went to press
and Lillian Budd sat back stunned to see her first book
become a best seller!

This remarkable lady was over fifty when she sat down
for that first night of writing. She continued at her full-
time job, maintained her home, and wrote two hours each
evening plus the hours from 7:00 a.m. to 7:00 p.m. Saturdays and Sundays ... "with just time out for church."

Lillian Budd now has ten books to her credit!

Physical Growth

Girls of 16 - 18 have attained an average height of 65

inches and an average weight of about 125 pounds. After twenty, many continue to grow in weight (to their own consternation) but not in height.

We will allude to this area of growth only in the terms of maintaining good health.

Spiritual Growth

Here, we ladies and girls have in common the leadership of our pastors and other Christian workers, access to good Christian books and periodicals, and *time* (that elusive element for which we have to plan) to spend with God's Word and in visiting with Him in prayer.

Unlike the physical growth which normally stops after adolescence, our spiritual growth should be a lifelong process.

Fanny Crosby (1820-1915) became blind at the age of six weeks and never regained her sight. She attended and later taught in a school for the blind. Among her multitude of friends were listed President Tyler, William Seward, William Cullen Bryant, President Polk and General Winfield Scott. This mentally alert lady continued to grow spiritually throughout her whole life. She left the world over 8000 hymns... among them are these old favorites: "Safe in the Arms of Jesus," "I Am Thine, O Lord," "Alas! and Did My Saviour Bleed?" and "Blessed Assurance."

We will, on occasion, consider a Bible verse... to see what it might mean to us as girls and ladies. In each instance this will be as a group study, where I merely toss in the verse, and then together, like a few friends over a cup of coffee, we will ask questions and give honest opinions ... certainly not the erudite answers of professional pastors with years of Greek and Bible study behind them. Their "solid" food we will "eat" on Sundays.

Social Growth

If it were important for God the Father to have His Son increase socially, as well as in these other areas, is it of less consequence for us to want our children and ourselves to improve socially? It would seem not. Yet, we must admit that there can be a tendency to slide over this area of development, thinking that any special effort might indicate conceit, or an unnecessary preoccupation with self or with the superficial.

This social growth, the fourth and last side of the "square" of growth accredited to our Lord, will be our main concern in this book. Social growth means the process of becoming more acceptable to other people. We use the word "process" advisedly because it is truly that...a *lifelong* process, in fact.

Charming You will deal with specifics . . . with easy-to-follow directions . . . with little cues to help you remember important points. We will explain each item carefully, discuss it together, and work on these ideas... *one point at a time.*

I would hope that you have already accustomed yourself to the tempo of *Charming You*. We will take it leisurely . . . with application . . . with understanding . . . and with lots of fun! Let's refuse to rush. Who would ever associate a rushing breathlessness with charm? Besides, I want to take the time to brush up on and to digest all of these different points too.

We will occasionally take time out for conversation, with varying degrees of relevancy.

Oh, that clock!

Excuse me, please! I'll be right back.

ᨤᨮᨤ

Hi! Thank you for waiting.

It was almost time for my husband to come home and I was still in my "typing" slacks, to which he had been over-exposed this past week.

It isn't that I'm expecting a repeat performance of last night's surprise bouquet of mums. But I don't care to have him feel short-changed by coming home to a dowdy wife after seeing grooming-conscious career girls all day. Besides, he's rather special!

Speaking of career girls, some of my friends to whom I will be alluding are just that, others are full-time home-makers, still others have combined the two professions. In some instances, the names of people have been altered, but the incidents or situations are factual.

Now, just for the fun of it, would you like to take a little pre-test?

Do you know:

1. how to *float* up and down stairs?
2. the correct body line-up?
3. how to gracefully pick up an object from the floor?
4. how to put on your coat in a never-fail, feminine manner?
5. how to gracefully get in and out of a car?

If you understand each of these well enough to teach someone else (not only *how* but also *why*) then you probably don't even need this refresher course.

But regardless of that, I sincerely hope that you will stay with us. As a musician likes to add to his musical experiences and a cook to her recipe file, so one who has already tasted the satisfaction of social know-how wants to continue in that area of growth.

So, please give your dog any attention he might need;

check your oven or whatever you might be concerned about, and then come back and join the group ... to concentrate on *Charming You.*

This course requires only two main props ... a full-length mirror and a Bible.

The first prop will let us see ourselves superficially, as others see us. The second prop will give us an in-depth impression of ourselves, through the eyes of our Creator.

As for the wall mirror, please don't think you cannot afford it. You really cannot afford *not* to have one for now and for the rest of your life. Hand and dresser mirrors are adequate for checking hairdos and dandruff on dresses. But what about an uneven hemline, a run in the back of your hose and your overall look?

Your mirror *could* be an impressive, bevelled-edged one with a copper-plated back. But an inexpensive one from a cutrate store would be equally functional.

Just allow your purse, your taste, and the spot in your home where it will be hanging to dictate the specific mirror you will purchase. Consider it an un-birthday gift to yourself ... or a surprise gift to your family or house.

As for the *place* to hang your mirror, you might like to consider some of these suggestions:

Mary and her family enjoy the beautiful full-length mirror and pier table in their living room ... right near the front door. Their guests also appreciate this.

Jane has an attractive full-length mirror at the end of her hall and a second inexpensive one attached to the inside of the hall closet door (on an adjoining wall). So, by opening the closet door, she is able to have a reflection of herself from all sides. She jokes that this can be rather demoralizing at times.

You might like yours on your bedroom wall or on your closet or bedroom door.

Regarding your second prop . . . the Bible. I assume that you already have one. But if you own just a New Testament, or just a Gospel of John, then we will wait while you go to your nearest book store for a copy of the Holy Bible including both the Old and New Testaments. You will want one in order to be a well-read person . . . if for no other reason.

Did you see the following full-page in the October 17, 1966 issue of *Newsweek* magazine?

ANATOMY OF A BEST SELLER

Is it drama?

Yes. It examines bravery, avarice, love, catastrophe, duty, war, ambition, hypocrisy, intrigue, sacrifice, adventure.

Is it history?

Yes. It unfolds some of the most significant pages of man's existence.

Is it biography?

Yes. It reveals the strengths and weaknesses of many famous men and women.

Is it poetry?

Yes. Its beauty, understanding and sensitivity are etched in the minds of millions.

Is it inspirational?

Yes. In just one chapter it contains ten steps that guarantee a successful life.

Is it well written?

Yes. It has a style and sweep and grandeur that have never been matched in the literary world.

It is all these and more!

That's why it has led the best seller list for 26,510 weeks.

Why not pick up a copy at your nearest bookstore?

Better yet, "pick it up" at your house of worship this week.

Its title: The Holy Bible.

ﾒ⌒⌒ﾒ

So much for our first visit.

It has been a pleasure to meet you all!

Now, let's make the necessary preparations for our next get-together . . . our first *work* session.

Let's Get Acquainted

Echoes and Overtones

The difference between a well-bred and an ill-bred man is this: one immediately attracts your liking, and the other your aversion. You love the one till you find reason to hate him. You hate the other till you find reason to love him.   SAMUEL JOHNSON

Don't let my life grow dull, Lord;
I want my heart to sing
The majesty of mountains,
The tint of bluebird's wing;
I want my ears to quicken
To brook song — rhythmic, low;
When stars come out at sunset,
I want my soul to grow;
Don't let my life grow dull!
                         AUTHOR UNKNOWN

Search me, O God, and know my heart!
Try me and know my thoughts!
                         PSALM 139:23 (RSV)

2

It's Saturday Night

The winsome story of *The Ugly Duckling* describes the change of costume from the dull grayish-brown of the cygnet (young swan) to the regal white covering of the year-old swan. This "queen," the inspiration of many poets and authors, owes her beauty to her unrivalled grace of movement and the meticulous appearance of her snowy white feathers.

These same two points, visual poise and meticulous cleanliness, also make up a lady's grace and beauty. But we have an advantage over the swan. Every swan must wait the same specified length of time to acquire that look of white elegance. Not so with us! We can each dictate the time and the degree of our "change of costume."

"But, dear, why don't *you* do like Arlene does?" sighed Mother, regarding us two first-graders. "Walk *around* the mud puddles, instead of right *through* them!"

True, Arlene's distaste for dirt did help her Mother's work load, but all I could think was, "Poor Arlene! Think of all the fun she misses! But, she's such a nice kid, otherwise."

Visual Poise and Meticulous Cleanliness are our twin ambassadors. They guarantee to make a "beauty" of any lady despite plain or unattractive natural features.

Three-year-old Barbie observed, "That lady we went to see this morning 'mells *brown*. If I go there aden, she'll probably 'mell, so what will I do? If she 'bites us over, I'll want to sit on your lap and she'll get close to you and I'll 'mell her and she 'mells *bad*."

Knowing that we are "squeaking" clean and well-groomed from the inside out, makes us feel "finished," alert, and reveling in the-world's-a-wonderful-place feeling!

Of course, you bathe often and are interested in having your clothes clean and well pressed. This material on personal cleanliness is included here merely to add a little spark to your present personal cleanliness routine, and to try to increase its efficiency by perhaps organizing it a bit better.

In this decade, when the prestige of a house can rise and fall with the number and the glamour of its bathrooms, and when the baths of all other ages might well seem remote and crude by contrast, it is an enlightening and shocking experience to read a good article on baths and bathing. *The World Book Encyclopedia*[1] tells of the baths of Caracalla, built during the reign of the Roman emperor of that name. These warm public baths were magnificent, and had room to hold 16,000 persons at one time.

We consider splash parties at the pool-side or beach,

[1] The material that follows is quoted and adapted from *The World Book Encyclopedia* copyright © 1967 Field Enterprise Educational Corporation.

with hamburgers, coke, popcorn, and records as the *now* thing; but in the 1600's there were many bathing resorts, with people spending as long as 124 hours (?) in the water. This was accompanied by bleeding, cupping (bringing blood to the surface with a cupping glass, with or without an incision in the skin), and the eating of huge quantities of food.

Soap supposedly had its origin at the sacrificial altars of the ancient Hebrews, where the wood ashes containing lye united chemically with the fat from the animal carcasses being burned there.

One of my early childhood memories is of Mother delving into the study of soap-making. Her enthusiasm was contagious. We children were as excited as she was about this new experiment going on in the basement. I recall that batch of soap as being velvety smooth and ever so white! And Mother's stock rose even higher in my estimation.

The Romans, who used sand and skin scrapers for their body cleaning, were not known to have had soap. The mountain people of Taiwan now wash with water and a stone, according to C. D. Holsinger of the Overseas Crusades. Soap, a luxury item, is their most appreciated gift. But we Americans? Ah! Soap of all colors, shapes, sizes, textures, scents, ingredients, and ingenious packaging! The market is surfeited with soaps, bubble baths, bath oils, bath powders and bath salts, until one's head swims with indecision.

Americans have heartily adopted the bath and have generously enlarged the circle around their calendar's *Saturdays* to include every day of the week.

Bathing is a cleansing habit, a relaxing experience, a tranquilizer requiring no doctor's prescription, an inexpensive therapy, a time for straightening out one's thoughts, a bad mood dissolver. Love that bath!

Some General Bath Suggestions

Relax and enjoy every bit of your bath, whether it's a three-minute scrub-down or a leisurely thirty-minute cleansing process.

About the best time for a bath is just before retiring.

If you're going to set your hair, do so before your bath and let the steam help clinch the set. Otherwise just tie your hair back and up with a ribbon or wear a shower cap.

Lubricate your face and neck and leave the cream on during your bath (unless your skin is oily).

Use warm (not hot) water.

Put in some water softener or detergent if your water is hard.

If you are planning to use bath oil or bath salts, add them as the water is running. Bath oil is good for dry skin. No bath oil on hand? Pour in some baby oil or mineral oil.

Choose your bath soap—mild for the average skin, lanolin for the dry.

Make a good lather from your soap and really use it all over your body (except your face). Rub well with your washcloth for good circulation. Cleanse and stimulate your back with a long-handled back brush. Remember your ears . . . inside and out. Wring out your washcloth before washing *inside* of ears.

Use pumice or a handbrush on any rough spots (elbows, heels, knees, or knuckles).

Do you have little bumps on your legs or arms or are they rough and scaly? Pour some table salt into your hand and rub it over the bumps.

Rinse, rinse, rinse! Don't leave any trace of the soap on you. Many people like to rinse off under the shower.

Now that you are spotlessly clean and thoroughly rinsed, pat yourself dry with a thick absorbent towel. In cold weather, give yourself a good rub-down with the towel. This will bring the blood to the surface and give you a new lease on life.

Tissue off your face cream.

Apply body or baby oil all over.

If you like to dust on bath powder, make sure your skin is perfectly dry first, so as not to clog the pores.

It pleased me to see a recent television commercial about baby powder for a lady's bath powder. I have used it for years. Probably you have too. Don't wait for them to advertise baby oil for adults. Use it now. They'll catch on!

There are other kinds of baths you can give yourself. Have you ever bathed in soda water? Baking soda, that is. Add about one cup of soda to your bath water and watch the dirt float away. You will be left feeling soft and refreshed.

Another item from your kitchen shelf which is good bath material is uncooked rolled oats. Put ½ cup of it on the center of a 12″ square of double thickness cheese-cloth; pull up the four corners; and secure them with a string or rubber band. Place this bag in the tub right under the spigot and let the water come full force. You will notice the water turn milky. Swish the bag around a few times, remove it from the water, and slide into your oatmeal bath. It will have a softening effect on your skin. The cheesecloth, but not the oats, could be reusable.

Personal Hygiene

Apply an underarm deodorant each morning.

And girls, you should be aware that deodorant powder (on napkins and on your body) can do for you what no other powder can! Be meticulously clean at *all* times.

Any blood-stained clothing should be immediately rinsed out in cold water. If some stain persists soak it in bleach and then wash the garment.

Skin Care

Elbows

Elbows constitute a perennial problem, — from the unclean, rough look of the young to the tired, wrinkled look of the mature.

Elbows remind me of a childhood ditty:

> I don't care how homely I are,
> I know that I'm no movie star;
> My face, I don't mind it
> For I am behind it.
> The folks in the front get the jar!

We could substitute:

> My elbows, I don't mind them
> For they are behind me.
> The folks in the back get the jar!

To forget our own elbows is an easy matter. We never hear from them (unless we happen to hit our "funny bone") and we never really see them (except as we look in a rear-view mirror). But, there they are . . . bending for us, regardless of our indifference to them.

Unrequited love!

Has anyone ever written "An Ode to the Elbow"?

1. *Keep them clean.* Wash elbows with warm suds and a hand brush or a pumice stone.

Sally uses cream cuticle remover on her elbows.

"My tube of cream cuticle remover states that it is

harmless to normal skin," she explains. "My skin is not hypersensitive. So, I use it on my cuticles each week *and* occasionally on my elbows. I wash and rinse it off well, and finish with an oil or cream application."

❧

The handsome young pilot showered frequently and *fast*, his route obviously detouring around his elbows.

One day when he was in the kitchen, his wife coyly said, "Turn around."

He complied (as would anyone to that sweetheart)!

"Now," she continued mysteriously, "put your hands on your hips."

"Hey! What kind of a game is this?"

But again — chuckling compliance!

What happened to him next couldn't possibly have happened before — unless perhaps in his pre-school days.

Did your mother ever scrub your dad's elbows with kitchen cleanser?

2. *Keep them bleached.* As you know, lemon is a good bleaching agent. You are baking, and your recipe calls for lemon juice? Use your elbows as the final lemon squeezers before throwing away the peels.

Put your left hand on your left shoulder, bring your elbow up in front, in line with your shoulder. Now, gingerly squeeze the lemon on your protruding elbow. Use the other lemon half on your right elbow.

Leave this "bonus" bleach on your elbows for a few minutes (while you finish your recipe). Wash and rinse off. Apply oil or cream.

Now that the lemon has done double duty, you should feel thrifty as you throw away the skins.

But wait . . . do you want them to do *triple* duty?

See pages 65 and 66, and 83.

3. *Keep them smooth.* Keep your elbows well lubricated with baby oil, cream and/or hand lotion.

Be generous when applying lotion to your hands, and develop the habit of wiping off the excess on your elbows. Always reach for your elbows after using hand lotion, as you reach for a towel after washing your hands!

Freckles

Freckles, caused by an accumulation of pigment (coloring matter) in the epidermis (outer layer of skin) are usually associated with exposure to the sunlight. Freckles can be one thing to the beholder and quite another to the owner.

One day, when I was still too young to see into the bathroom mirror without standing on something, I decided to try an experiment.

I was sick and tired of all those freckles on my face. Evelyn, my pretty, red-haired girl friend, had an unspotted complexion. My sister and brother had no freckles. Besides, the fact that Dad's childhood freckles showed no longer (except on his arms) was of no consolation to me.

"Wait *that* long before mine don't show? Why I'd be old enough to die!" I thought.

So there I was in the bathroom. The door was locked. I was about to try my first official experiment. I stood on the seat, leaned on the washbowl and stared at myself in the medicine cabinet mirror. There were those little brown villains — as clear and ugly as could be.

Rather than trying to eliminate all of them on the first day, I reasoned that the scientific approach would be to work on one limited area. If this met with the anticipated results, then a quick end to all the freckles would follow.

The bridge of my nose seemed the most logical place for this test patch.

If the cleansing powder Mother used could wipe out stains on the bathroom fixtures, why wouldn't it eliminate freckles, especially if I scrubbed hard . . . back and forth . . . back and forth . . . even when it hu-r-t . . .?

At school the next day, my test patch freckles did not show.

When the scab was gone . . . voila les freckles!

But time changes things.

Sooner or later, someone is bound to say, "Your freckles are cute!"

Then, too, not everyone could be chosen to do a song routine, *Freckle-Face Sal*, with one of the most popular guys in school.

Have you heard of freckle contests with the award going to the child with the most freckles? Seeing pictures of these smiling, "molasses-cookie-crumbed" faces in the morning paper gives the day a good start.

Skin stains

Lemon juice is a bleach. Apply it undiluted to the stain. Leave for a few minutes. Wash and rinse off.

Care of Superfluous Hair

Except for the soles of your feet, the palms of your hands, and your eyelids, there is a growth of fine, soft hair covering your whole body.

This is natural and unobjectionable.

The following suggestions have to do with the body hair which is embarrassing to the owner and perhaps objectionable to others.

Legs and underarms

It is impossible to be fastidious without removing the hair on one's legs and underarms. Carelessness about this affects others more than we realize. Just the other day, I overheard a group of high schoolers criticizing an adult who never shaves her legs.

This is one of those little niceties which must be cared for *consistently.*

Remove hair *after* bath if you shave with a regular razor.

Remove hair *before* bath if you use a depilatory, an electric razor, or pumice paper (for light hair growth).

If you nick the skin, apply an astringent or alum to check the bleeding.

Follow your shaving with a lubricant . . . any body oil or lotion.

Little Barbie closed a bedtime prayer with ". . . and we love Nana and Grandpa so much. We like to kiss them goodnight. We kiss Grandpa on the cheek because he has no whiskers there [he wore a mustache] . . . and neither does Mommy . . . but she does on her legs. Amen."

Yes, people are observant. Especially little girls who peek during their prayers.

Eyebrows

Our eyebrows play the important role of stopping some dust and perspiration from entering the eye. Fortunately their value does not stop with their utilitarian aspects.

Eyebrows are distinctive, individualistic! They are the "frames" for the most delicate and miraculous part of your body . . . your eyes.

I remember the Allen sisters at college. Their eyebrows

were prominent and grew straight across. These girls were beautiful and ladylike and took justifiable pride in their distinctive eyebrows.

There was an early-teen time when I painstakingly removed all of my eyebrows except the then current single hairline. (Fortunately, that style is gone, except for an occasional tweezer-happy lady.)

After church that Sunday morning, "Grandma" Brown, a dear old Welsh lady, worried aloud to my embarrassed but ever-loving mother: "Dear, dear! Do you suppose they will ever grow back?"

They did.

It was my first teaching position, and I was about to have my first professional tweezing job done. I emphasized that I wanted the brows to look neat and natural, with just the strays tweezed.

The beautician smiled, agreed, and tilted back my chair. This was before the days of piped-in stereo, so she turned on her own "record" about her recent operation, and beamed it toward the operator at the next chair. This "record" turned out to be a longplay monotone with no details omitted.

The two operations (her gall bladder and my eyebrows) were finished simultaneously. My chair was brought up to a regular position.

There, staring at me from the mirror, was the ghost of my former de-eyebrowed experience. I sat stunned, remembering that rich Welsh voice: "Dear, dear! Do you suppose they will ever grow back?"

So, eyebrows are the frames for our eyes? Then those frames I saw in the mirror were understated, not with the elegant simplicity as from an exclusive little frame shop, but rather like cheap little frames picked up at a rummage sale.

Don't do this to yourself — and don't allow anyone else to do it to you. Your eyebrows are distinctive; keep them that way. Tweeze only the stray hairs growing *below* your eyebrows and across the bridge of your nose. Before and after tweezing, swab the area with cotton dipped in alcohol or witch hazel.

Do you wear glasses and find it difficult to see close-up without them? Try one of the following ideas for tweezing your eyebrows:

1. Remove your glasses and look through a magnifying glass into a mirror.

2. With your left hand (if you're right-handed), tip your glasses at an angle, so that you are looking through only your left lens, with the right lens above or below your right eye, leaving it free to work on.

Look through your right lens while tweezing your left eyebrow.

If you don't already own a magnifying mirror, I would suggest that you make this small investment. An inexpensive one can be found in any variety store. You will especially like the kind that stands up on your dresser, with a regular mirror on one side and a magnifying one on the other.

Here's a grooming treatment for eyebrows:

1. Apply Vaseline[2] Petroleum Jelly to your brows and rub, brush, or comb them *backwards*, towards your nose.

[2] *Vaseline* is the registered trademark of Chesebrough-Pond's Inc.

(They will look wild. You'll remind yourself of a seasoned politician!)

2. Now, brush your brows straight up, toward your hair line. (This time you'll have a frightened look.) Use an eyebrow brush, a discarded toothbrush or a fine-toothed comb for this.

3. Now for the final touch — and this works *magic!* With your eyebrow brush, gently outline only the very top of your brows, starting from the inside (by your nose) and working along to the end of your brows (by your temples).

Don't you like the neat, wide-eyed effect of that little 1-2-3 quickie? Then how about adding it to your daily beauty routine?

By the way, "Vaseline" never hurts anyone's eyelashes, either. It imparts a nice sheen, and certainly would not hinder their growth.

Esther, my meticulous friend who worked for an optometrist, helped alert me to the inconsistency of anyone's allowing grimy-looking glasses to frame potentially beautiful eyes. Don't be like a home-owner who paints his house with an obnoxious color, or who is indifferent to a weatherbeaten exterior. He can retreat behind his walls, but the inflicted neighbors don't have that privilege.

If you wear glasses, keep them clean. Just wash them in warm, sudsy water.

Facial hair

If you are one of the many with this problem and your budget makes electrolysis by an expert prohibitive, you can safely remove unwanted facial hair by carefully following the directions accompanying a depilatory. They suggest a patch test to determine if your skin is too sensitive for their product.

Some ladies prefer bleaching to removing the facial hair. With either process, it is important to read and follow the directions of the product.

Never shave any hair on your face or arms.

Nasal hairs

The hairs lining the inside of the nose are important to help sift out dust and particles from the inhaled air. But those hairs which protrude are offensive and should be cut — *never tweezed!*

They are best removed with a small pair of *blunt-edged* scissors. These, unlike manicure or any other scissors, insure against any nicking of the skin. They can be purchased at drug stores. One pair should last you a lifetime.

Your husband or father will also want to use them, much oftener than you, probably. You might check around his ears, too — and snip off any strays there.

The Weekly Beauty Binge

Every day you go through a personal cleanliness routine, but once a week there is that special time! It's a date with yourself, when you take care of your non-daily personal beauty matters — manicure, pedicure, shampoo and shaving.

Thursday evening is ideal for the working lady or school girl, because the timing is just right to make her especially prepared for the weekend's activities.

If you are a housewife, alone during the day, you might prefer Friday morning or afternoon when you have the house completely to yourself and are assured of no interruptions.

But whatever your time choice, remember that this weekly date with yourself is to be kept just as conscientiously as a date with someone else. Refuse any other appointments at that time.

Enjoy that feeling of extra cleanliness while you anticipate the weekend. Forget your problems and luxuriate in the different steps which constitute this *Complete Clean-Up Campaign.*

1. *Shampoo your hair* (see page 80). Now, wrap your hair in a towel, or set it, for your bath time.

2. *Bathe* (see page 30). Enjoy the luxury of your bath. Do you like to sing as you soak? You prefer a radio? *Warning* . . . never touch a radio while you're in the tub. You'd probably never know what tune had been playing!

After the bath, pat some freshener on your face. In warm weather, treat yourself to a cool freshener (vinegar, or refrigerated water or freshener). If you use vinegar, be sure to keep it out of your eyes.

3. *Shave legs and underarms* (see page 36).

4. *Facial* (see page 47ff).

5. *Pedicure* (see page 70).

6. *Manicure* (see page 66).

7. *Set your hair* in its accustomed style, or try a new hair-do.

❧❧❧

My college days came during the depression, when twenty-five cents for a set seemed fair remuneration to me. I enjoyed visiting with the kids who came to my room. Besides, setting hair in waves was a satisfying artistic experience (which I've never felt about rollers).

One day Peg, an attractive blond, agreed to let me try a new style on her. It was featured in a magazine, with accompanying sketches showing how to arrange series of pin curls just on the top, with the rest of the hair set in the usual waves.

The pin curls were supposed to comb out into three soft, wispy "rolls."

But, I hadn't taken into consideration the fact that her hair had not been cut for this new style. Last spring, while visiting with her in Atlanta, she reminded me of those bulky, defiant "top-knots" which had greeted her that next morning.

What would one do about such a "hair-raising" experience in those "olden" days, before hair sprays, dryers, and such?

Peg quickly "washed that set right out of her hair" and appeared at her early morning class looking as if she'd just left the pool.

Yes, dynamite in a magazine can degenerate to a dud in reality!

Peg married her college sweetheart. You might well have read his book, *Prison Is My Parish,* the Story of Park Tucker as told to George Burnham, published by Revell. Or you might have seen them on Ralph Edwards' "This Is Your Life" television program. Martha Doran, a college friend, said, "No matter where you go you're bound to meet someone who knows Park Tucker. Why when we were in Alaska . . . and Japan . . ." And so it goes. Park recently finished twenty years as the protestant chaplain at the Federal Penitentiary in Atlanta.

꼰꼰꼰

8. *Retire.* Slip into bed with a thoroughly clean body and an equally clean conscience!

If yours is a daytime complete clean-up campaign, you might like to take a little nap before dressing.

It's Saturday Night

Echoes and Overtones

"Cleanliness is indeed next to Godliness," is *not* a quote from the Bible as is generally believed. Rather it is taken from a "Sermon on Dress" by John Wesley (1703-1791).

❧❧❧

Wash me, and I shall be whiter than snow.
PSALM 51:7

❧❧❧

For cleanness of body was ever esteemed to proceed from a due reverence to God, to society, and to ourselves.
FRANCIS BACON

❧❧❧

I will both lay me down in peace and sleep:
for thou, Lord, only makest me dwell in safety.
PSALM 4:8

3

Look This Way, Please!

Complexions vary from normal through oily or dry to a combination of these and on to problem skin with acne or allergies. So there can be no one specific facial care for everyone to follow.

But cleanliness is basic and its importance cannot be overstressed, both for maintaining a good normal complexion and for improving one which needs it.

Washing Your Face

Work up a generous lather in lukewarm water. Now, with rotating finger-tip motions, gently massage this lush lather into your neck and face, starting at your throat and working up to your forehead. Give special attention to your chin and the creases around your nose.

Rinse off repeatedly with tepid water, until the soap is completely removed. Soap, after it has done its cleansing work, is no longer a welcome guest. If allowed to stay on, it busies itself at clogging pores and drying skin.

Pat your clean face gently with an absorbent towel. For stimulation, use a final ice water rinse or gingerly pat your face with your fingers until your face tingles. You have probably observed that the password has been "gently" (except for that last point). This admonition is not just for those who are no longer youngsters. It is for every person reading this book.

Agnes, an attractive golfer, whose casual wools looked so right on her, was watching me dry my face.

"Have you no pity on your poor face?" she scolded. "Wait until you're my age, and you will be drying it ever so gently."

She occasionally referred to our age discrepancy. Actually, there was none, except chronologically. Because of her interests and outlook, Agnes epitomized the true spirit of youth.

We just laughed and continued our previous conversation. But in the back of my mind, I was assured that this would not happen to me. True, others grew older, but I just would not.

Well, for the sake of any readers who prefer the sequel spelled out for them, the calendars *did* refuse me a life residency in that magic land of the late teens and early twenties.

A desperate clinging to youth can be pathetic!

I've never read that Grandma Moses resented her deep facial lines. To us who are grateful for her ability to depict Americana, her face represents a full life, character, beauty and love. Long may her shadow stretch across the United States!

Oily Skin Care

Wash three or four times a day (as above) with medicated soap or with a special cleansing lotion containing hexachlorophene. Follow this each time with an astringent.

Enjoy fruits and vegetables.

Resist fat and fried foods.

Soak in some sunshine, if possible.

Shampoo your hair often.

Dry Skin Care

In the morning, cleanse your face with lather from gentle castile soap or with a cleansing cream. Follow this with a warm water rinsing.

Pat your face dry immediately. Allowing the water to dry on your skin aggravates the dry condition.

Now apply baby oil or some other lubricating lotion or a good moisturizer.

Before retiring, apply a cream base.

You could probably eat more animal fats, as in butter and milk.

Problem Skin

If the above suggestions, plus enough sleep and exercise, still leave you unsatisfied with your skin condition, consult a dermatologist. He can give you professional help for acne or a list of foods to avoid for any allergies.

If you have *acne,* you are not alone, especially among adolescents. Acne is an infection of the sebaceous (oil) glands of the skin. First there is a blackhead (an accumulation of dirt and dried grease in an oil gland). Bacteria working on that blackhead causes a pimple. This in turn may develop into an abscess and may even leave a scar.

The two main precautions for acne are 1) cleanliness of the skin and 2) cutting down on the activity of the oil glands.

Wash your face often, using the above suggestions for

care of oily skin. If you are a washcloth user, you can further frustrate the bacteria by using a fresh washcloth each time.

And further:

> Keep your hands off your face.
> Do not scratch the acne.
> Exercise . . . much!
> Eat fruits, vegetables, and lean meats.
> Politely refuse candies and rich desserts.
> Work and exercise will help use up oils from your glands.

The application of drugs (prescribed by your doctor) will slow down the oil secretion.

Avoid facial foundations and powder.

In time, this too, like wearing braces on your teeth, will pass.

Believe it!

In the meantime, pasting yourself against a wall is not the answer. But cleansing your face, walking, exercising, eating wisely and enjoying life and other people *is!*

Besides, you will have a fringe benefit — the habit of facial cleanliness, which will stand you in good stead for the rest of your life.

Facials

Enjoy the treat of a home facial!

There are many commercial facials, but don't overlook a few good ones from your own kitchen. Have you ever had a facial from one of these: egg white, buttermilk, whipped cream, egg yolk, oatmeal, or honey? The last is my favorite because of its fragrance and *flavor* (it's lickin' good!)

With any of these "kitchen" facials, you could follow these steps:

1. Cleanse the face and neck with face cream.
2. Tissue off the cream.
3. Gently cover the face and neck with the facial material. (For oatmeal, tie a handful of dry rolled oats in cheesecloth. Immerse this in warm water. Pat your face with this bag. The facial will look dry and powdery.)
4. Allow about fifteen minutes for it to work.
5. Rinse it off with tepid water.
6. Finish with cold water.

Do this and you and your face will have an extra glow! Here are a few special "frosting" ideas for this "cake."

If you were registered at a luxury beauty spa or farm, I understand that you would be served breakfast in bed; would have massages and sunlamp treatments; be given professional helps in make-up and hair-styling; you would exercise to music and swim in opulent pools; your calorie-right meals would be served elegantly and you would receive V.I.P. treatment from each person serving you throughout your stay.

So, your home setting lacks the decor and equipment of a beauty spa? So does mine! But that does not hinder us from borrowing some of their ideas. Add a little atmosphere and ingenuity to your home facial and make it a de luxe treatment for the queen (or princess) of your home!

Ready?

First . . . do you own a slant board?

A slant board has several advantages to offer you. Lying with your head lower than your feet is working against gravity, so that the flow of your blood is reversed. Having the blood rush to your head will give you a certain exhilaration surpassed only by standing on your head.

Sagging muscles? Puffy feet or legs? Let those who

will stand on their heads. Why don't you just lazily stretch out on a slant board and accomplish the same result?

As a child, I used to stand on my head so long at a time that my mother became concerned. She finally limited me to the count of 100. Amazing how slowly I could count. I'm not sure yet just what I was trying to prove.

One third of a century later, the subject of standing on heads came up in my present family.

"Why, there's nothing to it!" I bragged, walking to the middle of our living room floor and proceeding to show this modern generation a thing or two!

I did! So now we have thick padding under our carpeting and "slant board" heads my Christmas list to my workshop oriented husband. But so far there has been no evidence of work on any board — slant or otherwise. Perhaps I should have him read these pages.

A slant board is also a good lazyman's exerciser because the foot straps cooperate to hold your feet down while you come up to a sitting position and then continue forward until you touch your toes. (Watch your knees . . . you're bending them!)

Exercising on a slant board gives you double dividends, like a "two-for-the-price-of-one" sale!

If you don't own a slant board, you can contrive one in a few seconds.

Take your ironing board. Leave it collapsed and lay it on the floor. Now raise the narrow end about fifteen inches above the floor (supported on catalogues or big books). If you are not on carpeting and your floor is slippery, you could butt the wide end of the board against the wall.

Next . . .

1. Put on some of your favorite long-play records or turn on your favorite radio station.

2. Stretch out on your slant board (head lower than feet).

3. Close your eyes and apply a tea bag (dipped in warm water and then squeezed) to each eye. These give your eyes a restful treatment, too.

Now, listen to the music . . . relax . . . feel your facial mask drawing as it dries. Ah-h-h!

As I mentioned before, honey is my favorite facial. It smells so good! Honey . . . bees . . . wild flowers . . . soft summer breezes! What commercial facial could rival honey for built-in nostalgia? Honey on hot biscuits . . . peanut butter and honey sandwiches. Or, maybe you have some special honey memories? Our family has two.

⚜

Two sisters from New York City were annoyed by occasional honey bees in their rural Cape Cod summer home. My father, who owned bee paraphernalia and a smoke gun, agreed to look into it. We three children rode along.

No one was prepared for the onslaught of those disturbed bees that swarmed out after Dad had removed some siding.

My sister and the one lady who had been watching from an upstairs window, dove into bed and covered their heads with the bedding. The other lady shot into the house, leaving most of her frenzied attackers outside.

We two little ones ran screaming to Dad, regardless of the fact that the strongest concentration of bees was around him. His bee hat and gloves completely protected him, but his gun was a weak weapon against the horde dive-bombing us.

I shall always remember that agonizing mixture of compassion and utter helplessness of Dad's "Go away! Go away, sweethearts! Run to the road . . . the road!"

At the road, we threw dust on our heads as Dad told us to. As we stumbled along the road to the first farm house, we kept looking back for Dad's reassuring waves. By the time we arrived there we had left our last assailant behind.

Mrs. Walker, our good friend and neighbor, removed stinger after stinger from our heads. No, not one single sting on our bare legs or feet . . . just a *few* on our faces . . . but *dozens* on our heads.

At home that night, Mother and Dad removed even more of the bees' "calling cards" from our heads.

Some years later, Dad was finishing another pastorate in a village about thirty miles from the "bee house." Of all the available houses in that area, which one do you think he chose to buy for his retirement years? None other!

༺◦༻

A jolly Welsh friend of ours was helping Dad move a bee hive one night.

"Are you sure this thing is all plugged up tight?" joked Stan.

"Oh, sure. Everything's tight! Besides, bees are always quiet at night," reassured my Father.

I was trudging along beside them, holding the lantern.

"Ye-ow-w!!" screamed Stan, letting the hive crash down, and slapping his sleeve which had suddenly taken on life.

༺◦༻

Now that your relaxing facial is finished (and without one single bee sting) rinse it off and pat yourself dry.

How about a leisurely cranberry-juice-on-the-rocks? Or would you prefer sipping a cup of hot tea . . . from one of your best china teacups?

Luxury! With no big tab . . . and only yourself to tip.

Not long ago, a certain prominent young American made headlines by leaving no tip at a certain beauty spa. The more I think about home treatments, the better they seem!

✺

I once had a commercial facial mask which turned chalk white as it dried. One day, while I was stretched out under this stark white mask, the doorbell rang. My first thought was of some salesman who would have to be without a customer at this address.

When the doorbell rang again, I decided it must be a friend, so I started up. Then I heard knocking at the door. So I rushed, anxious to surprise whichever friend it might be.

I did a Phyllis Diller stance and opened the door . . . .

How persistent are the census takers in *your* city?

Do you suppose this one wrote *"haunted"* for her report on our house?

"Vaseline" facial

Two days ago, I looked in vain for anything to do with beauty on the label of our big Vaseline Petroleum Jelly jar. Only . . . "A soothing dressing for burns, cuts, scrapes, detergent hands, diaper rash, chafing, and sunburn."

Certainly they must be aware of its facial use. Why don't they advertise that? I wondered. *I think I'll write them.*

That letter wasn't written because that very night there was a "Vaseline"-sponsored TV commercial demonstrating this very thing. You will certainly want to try it. Here it is:

1. Heat some "Vaseline" by putting a dish holding a little into boiling water . . . as you would for heating a baby's bottle.

2. Apply this softened, heated "Vaseline" to your face and neck.

3. Cover your face and neck with an absorbent towel wrung out of hot water.

4. Now, let the steam and the "Vaseline" work for you.

5. Wipe off the excess "Vaseline," but leave on a little coating for your night's sleep. Your face will be ever so smooth!

I'll admit that these home facials lack the exotic names (unless you make up some of your own) and the impressive price tags of many commercial facials, but after all, it is the *ingredients* of a facial which produce the results.

During some class sessions, the thought would flash through my mind, "Here I'm *paying* someone to tell me of some homemade beauty recipes which Mother taught us as children."

We ladies learned many helpful ideas at a cooking school yesterday. Mr. Eddie Doucette, Consultant Chef with the IGA Food Stores, demonstrated among other things how to cut a tomato, orange or lemon into saw-toothed halves by making a series of V-shaped incisions all around its circumference. It is a simple operation and the artistic result has eye appeal.

"People eat through their eyes, you know," wisely explained Mr. Doucette.

Oddly enough, I had "discovered" this cutting technique on my own, just a few weeks ago.

Steam facial

It's strange how we can consider ourselves so original, and then discover that we are not alone. "Strange" in a warm, friendly way because of the united interdependent feeling it gives one.

Interesting, too, how we build on others' foundations, sometimes deliberately, at other times unwittingly.

Once, I decided that if a resourceful friend of mine could use an electric frying pan as her bedside steamer for a head cold, perhaps I could build on that idea and . . . !

My husband obligingly cut the bottom out of a large empty plastic jug and then cut a generous sloping oval out of its top. When placed in the electric frying pan, the water keeps the plastic from melting and the steam cooperatively floats up through the dissected jug to caress your face.

You can easily regulate the amount of steam on this portable (bedroom, bathroom or wherever you choose) homemade *sauna facial*.

Cleanse your face well before steaming it. Steam it for about ten minutes, and then cleanse it some more. It's an exhilarating experience! Finish with your favorite lubricant, perhaps baby oil, or a moisturizing cream.

I like to apply a thin coat of "Vaseline" (no need to preheat it) after a steaming session and then steam again . . . this time through the "Vaseline."

Experimenting with this homemade contrivance has been fun. And none of it would have happened, if Louise Troup, the Executive Director of the Pioneer Girls hadn't shared her cool cold idea!

Egg facials

You're making a meringue? Don't put the yolks in the refrigerator for some indeterminate future! Give yourself an egg yolk facial right now.

Merely cover your face and neck with a layer of egg yolk. It will dry rather quickly. Your face will look touched by Midas, and it will *feel* just that tight when the yolk dries!

But tonight, while you're all enjoying that meringue, you will feel and look just that much smarter.

You have a little egg white on hand? Spread it over your face and neck. This, too, will dry quickly. It will give you a tight, glassy-looking facial.

More tips

Any one of these facials can work while *you* are working, if you don't want to take the time right now to lie down on your slant board.

❦

Have a container to hold your used tea bags. True, they will look as unappetizing as some old fried bacon . . . but, you'll be using them for your closed eyes . . . not your mouth.

When you're ready, just swish them through tepid water, squeeze them out, and let them work on your eyes during your slant board siesta. Yes, fresh tea bags will work, too!

❦

Slant board time, like bath time, does not have to be a time to turn off your mind. You can think, plan or memorize (stick that new list of French words on your bathroom wall with plasti-tak, and strive for an A on that quiz).

Make-Up

The use of make-up was no innovation of some enterprising American, although retail sales of cosmetics and toiletries in the United States amount to over $3 billion a year (*Newsweek,* November 20, 1967, p. 34).

Last week while visiting the beautiful Toledo Art Museum, we were amused at the collection of *unguentaria* (it just *sounds* like a medicine). These ornate glass holders, resembling two to four crude test tubes fused together and having a common handle, were from Syria and belonged to the period from the fourth to the sixth centuries A.D. They held cosmetic unguents — mainly black and red — on ladies' dressing tables.

Cosmetics were used long before that, however. Physicians in ancient Egypt, according to *The World Book Encyclopedia,* supplied and used cosmetics, until they became too busy, and tradesmen took over supplying the increasing demand. Perhaps the most famous person known to have used cosmetics was Cleopatra, the last queen of Egypt.

〰️

A most attractive local lady wears a little lipstick . . . and that's it! Not even powder. She has black eyebrows which she does not tweeze out of character, a dresden complexion with a hint of natural color and always an interested, outgoing manner. Her family, including her college son, must be proud of her natural beauty.

A young neighbor fits into this natural beauty category, too. It's refreshing to look at a lady's face and actually see *skin*, especially when it's on a face like Bernie's or Mary's.

Most of us who share Jack Benny's perennial thirty-nine just do not have the face to go without make-up. The secret is to play it down, keep it to the minimum and apply it in good light.

Consult a professional beautician regarding the shades best for you and the proper method of application. This is both a time- and money-saver as it eliminates your own trial and error methods of cosmetic purchasing.

In applying lipstick:

1. Outline your lips with a lip brush.
2. Fill in the outline with your lipstick.
3. Blot your lips with tissue. (Lipstick smears on a cup, glass, or napkin fall into the category of mud tracks on carpeting.)

I recall Mother's concern for a lady who was speaking in our church. This speaker was a dear, consecrated lady whose pale face in no way matched her healthy, vibrant faith. Mother tried in vain to convince her that a touch of rouge, by making her look healthier, would call less attention to herself.

This reminds me, in reverse, of a night club story. Some women, wearing their make-up almost audibly, noticed a lady at another table who was wearing absolutely no make-up.

"Disgusting!" deprecated one of them, "Some women will do anything to call attention to themselves!"

Care of Your Teeth

"Please don't say anything about my two front teeth," begged seventh-grade Mary.

Mary, one of the prettiest girls in our school, was the

one whose name I had drawn for some guessing game. Her wavy hair, pretty face, and sparkling brown eyes had not escaped my notice, but her two front teeth had, until now that she was calling attention to them. Her two upper central incisors overlapped a little.

Relieved at the assurance that they would not be mentioned, she seemed surprised that I had never noticed her overlapping front teeth.

※

Mine was a different problem!

Mother, envisioning her younger daughter's future . . . behind the footlights . . . seated at a concert grand piano . . . consulted with our dentist as to what could be done about my teeth separations, especially that between my two front teeth.

The dentist obligingly tied strings tightly around the two upper central incisors. Later, the string was replaced by a wide gold band. These were not strictly the happiest weeks in my childhood.

The day for the unveiling arrived. The gold band was gone, and the dentist promptly handed me a mirror. My two front teeth were together — at least at the bottom.

They stayed that way . . . for awhile.

If dentistry's advancements of today had been in existence in Mary's and my teen-age years, we would undoubtedly have joined the club (the prestige club!) and would have been keeping appointments with our orthodontists!

Granted, my smile is a somewhat punctuated one! But with only a devoted family and a few friends "applauding" from the "audience" side of my *desk* light, it doesn't really matter that much. I've even been told that mine is a million-dollar smile. (Could they have been referring to all the space between those digits?)

I've been reading lately of orthodontic work on older people, up to the age of 65 years. A dentist being interviewed recently predicted that more and more people will be keeping their own teeth all of their lives.

Oral hygiene

1. *Keep your teeth sparkling clean!* "You're not well dressed, unless you're wearing a healthy smile." (Chicago Dental Association)

2. *The tooth brush.* The American Dental Association says: "A good toothbrush should have: a flat brushing surface, firm, resilient bristles (the dentist can advise on stiffness) and a head small enough to permit access to the surface of all the teeth."

Don't limit yourself to one; have at least two. It's a good idea to distribute them to each wash bowl (Yes, the kitchen sink, too) so there will always be one available.

Before purchasing an electric toothbrush, consult your dentist as to the type to buy. My oral surgeon recommends just one type.

3. *The dentifrice.*

Any accepted commercial dentifrice. There are many good ones from which to choose. You may secure a list of approved dentrifices published annually by the American Dental Association, Chicago, Illinois.

Home dentifrices. Soda and/or salt are effective. This dentifrice is purely functional . . . nothing spectacular in the area of tantalizing tastes, sweet aromas, or sudsy foam . . . just a clean-looking and fresh-smelling mouth!

I knew a doctor who used no dentifrice but this.

4. *Method of brushing.* The general rule is *from the*

gums to the biting edge:

   Uppers . . . from gums *down* to biting edge.

   Lowers . . . from gums *up* to biting edge.

Brush inside and outside.

   Biting edge . . . brush with a rotating motion.

   Spend time. Remember that each tooth has five surfaces to be cleaned . . . the front, the back, two sides, and the biting edge.

   Massage and stimulation is good for the gums.

   Brush your tongue. This seems to be the forgotten member of the mouth when it comes to oral cleansing instructions. Yet my mouth cleansing feels "finished" only after the top of my tongue has also been brushed.

   It *is* part of the mouth . . . and a rather substantial part, too.

   One of my friends kidded me; "Brush your *tongue?* That's like saying, 'And remember, girls, a good housekeeper always cleans out her key-holes!' "

And, furthermore

   The sooner you brush your teeth after having eaten, the less time your food has to do damage to your teeth.

   Whether you now have your original teeth, or a set purchased from your dentist is immaterial. The important thing is to *keep them clean* . . . for the smile that "wins friends and influences people."

   Salt and/or soda dissolved in water provides a good mouthwash.

   All of the news media reminds us of the importance of not offending others by unpleasantly "fogging" the air they're inhaling. It is true that we can have halitosis without being aware of it ourselves.

   We used to sing: (Tune, *Boola! Boola!*)

Hal-i-to-sis!
Hal-i-to-sis!
Drives your clo-sest
Friends a-way!

So, use preventive measures. There are many good mouthwashes on the market. "An apple a day will keep the doctor away; and an onion a day will keep everyone away."

The teeth of primitive people are usually much stronger than those of our civilized races because of the quantity of starches and sugars in our diet.

If you're in a situation where you cannot brush your teeth after eating, at least rinse your mouth well with water to help dislodge food particles.

Have a dental appointment every six months.

You've bought extra toothbrushes for vacations and overnights, and now you don't know to whom they belong? You can sterilize them in zephorin chloride, an inexpensive solution from the drug store, convenient to have on hand for several sterilizing purposes.

Always carry a toothbrush in your purse.

Others can share their food and lodging, but, a toothbrush?

Rather than just a toothbrush in its case, why not buy a little zipped case (plastic, cloth, or leather)? This "survival kit" holding toothbrush, aspirin, band-aids, tissue, safety pins, a miniature spray mouthwash, and a dime would fit neatly into your purse.

❦

Now, four months and several hints later, I am the proud owner of a neat home-made slant board covered with carpeting over sponge rubber underliner. The base? Cut from the top of an old buffet. All of these materials were on hand, so the only expense was $1.25 for the hardware.

Slant Board Specifications

1 — ¾″ plyboard 16″ x 70″
1 — ¾″ plyboard 11″ x 14″
1 pair Amerock Nickel hinge type support
1 pair 1½″ hinges
1 piece 16″ x 70″ underliner (sponge rubber, jute liner, blanketing, etc.)
1 piece 22″ x 76″ covering (carpeting, plastic, terrycloth, etc.)
1 piece 5″ x 30″ matching carpeting for footstrap
Furniture type tacks

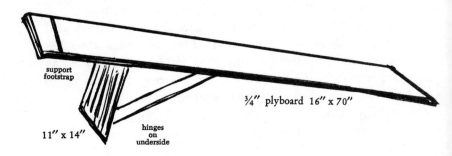

support
footstrap

¾″ plyboard 16″ x 70″

11″ x 14″   hinges
on
underside

Look This Way, Please!

Echoes and Overtones

Beautiful faces are those that wear
Whole-souled honesty printed there.
ELLEN P. ATTERTON, *Beautiful Things*

෴

A man's wisdom maketh his face to shine.
ECCLESIASTES 8:1

෴

Face to Face

Face to face with Christ my Saviour.
Face to face — what will it be,
When with rapture I behold Him,
Jesus Christ Who died for me?

What rejoicing in His presence,
When are banished grief and pain;
When the crooked ways are straightened,
And the dark things shall be plain.
CARRIE E. BRECK (1855-1934)

4

Ten Fingers, Ten Toes

The first time that I was really aware of a lady's hands was when a gentleman from the deep South took my big sister's hand, slowly bent over it, and actually kissed that sixteen-year-old upstate New York hand! He was an "older" man — must have been at least twenty!

What an aura she wore for days! I treated her with the deference we both felt she deserved. I too felt the desecration when *that* hand had to submit to the mundane confines of a dishpan.

Graceful Hands

For grace in hand movement, always lead with your wrist.

The hand is most beautiful when seen in profile.

When seated, don't let your hands appear "busy"; have them resting quietly on your lap.

General care of your hands

Wash hands often and form the habit of pushing back the cuticle with the towel as you dry.

Use hand lotion or cream after having hands in water. Rub the excess on your elbows.

Keep hand lotion at each sink in your house.

Keep your nails clean and well manicured (have an extra emery board by the telephone and television).

Apply baby oil, a hand cream, or even castor oil on them at night.

Give them a special treatment once a week, or when they are chapped or cracked: warm your night oil or vaseline before applying it; massage it in well, rubbing upward from finger tips to the wrist; cover with a loosely fitting pair of cotton gloves for bed.

Rubber gloves protect hands from hot water and strong detergents. For an on-the-job beauty treatment, cream your hands before putting on the gloves. The heat from the water will help the cream penetrate your skin.

Cotton or leather gloves cut down on calluses from hard work like raking leaves, or mowing the lawn.

Before doing dirty tasks (potting plants, shining shoes, polishing silver) dig all of your nails into a wet bar of soap. The soap under your nails will then have priority over the dirt and they will both wash off effortlessly after the job is finished.

Lemon juice will help banish stains.

Give yourself a weekly manicure.

A good hand exercise is to let your hands go limp and then shake them hard and fast until they tingle. You can do this while sitting or standing.

Another good hand exercise is to alternate between a tight hand clench and a quick thrusting out of all fingers. Do this several times in a row.

Apply hand lotion before going out in the cold.

Wear gloves when you go out; always during winter and on "glove" occasions during the warm months.

〴⧫〵

Your weekly home manicure

If you are wearing nail polish, remove it with polish remover, stroking from the nail base to the nail tip, being careful to keep the dissolving polish from the skin.

File the nails with the coarse side of an emery board (do not use a metal file). File from the outside corner of the nail to the middle. Work for the pleasing oval look, not pointed or blunt. Hold the emery board at a right angle to the edge of your nail to help insure against the nail's thin layers later separating from each other.

Buffing the edges now or flicking them with the fine side of the emery board also helps eliminate layering.

Heat two or three tablespoons of some oil (baby, peanut or vegetable) or use regular hand cream or vaseline. Massage this well into your hands and nails. Massage in little circular motions from the wrists to the tip of each finger. Now, hold the hands upright and work down the length of each finger several times, as if putting on tight gloves.

(This previous step is not essential to a manicure. Just a deluxe feature, when you have the time!)

Immerse your hands in warm sudsy water for several minutes to further soften your cuticle.

You may use a nail brush to help scrub away dead cuticle.

To remove stubborn stains, use pumice stone or lemon juice.

Rinse and dry hands carefully, pushing back cuticle with towel.

Apply a cuticle remover with a cotton-tipped orange stick. (Remove just a little cotton from a cotton ball and twist it around the end of the orange stick.)

Use the blunt end of the orange stick to gently ease your cuticle back into an oval shape.

Use nail scissors on any thickened skin at the top corners of your nails.

Never cut the cuticle.

Now, wash your hands again and dry thoroughly.

For a clean natural look:

a. Apply some talcum powder to your nails and buff them with a nail buff. This produces a natural lustre and the stimulation helps strengthen the nails.

b. Or, apply two coats of colorless nail polish or a sealer.

c. Apply a little nail white under the nails.

If you prefer colored nail polish, you probably have graceful, pretty hands. The color will feature them, make them conspicuous.

a. Apply two base coats.

b. Follow with two coats of your color choice (allowing ten minutes between coats). Paint with one stroke down center of nail and then one on either side of it. Remove just a hairline of the polish from the tip of each nail with the pad of your thumb.

1) To give the illusion of length, paint the entire nail — moon and finger tip.

2) To make a nail appear shorter, do not paint the moon or tip.

3) To make a nail appear narrower, do not paint way to the side edges.

c. Finish with a sealer coat.

Further nail pointers

A split nail can be mended with scotch tape, flesh-colored adhesive tape, or a commercial mender.

Use a commercial hard-nail coating on fragile nails.

Daily taking an envelope of unflavored gelatin in bouillon or in fruit juice has helped many ladies strengthen fragile nails. Gelatin is high in protein and has no sugar content.

Take Care of Your Feet

Valeda the Glass Lady talked to a group of us last week!

This life-size model of a woman, cast in plexiglass at Cologne, Germany, was flown to Chicago, where several miles of electrical wiring were installed, enabling her to "speak." She is probably the "star" of the excellent exhibits at the Health Museum in Hinsdale, Illinois.

On the wall of her little theatre, where the glass lady stands on the stage, is written:

> Man wonders over the restless sea;
> The flowing waters — the sight of the sky —
> And forgets that of all wonders,
> Man himself is the most wonderful.
> ST. AUGUSTINE

During Valeda's talk to school children and her other talk to adults, the lights of the room are turned off, and the audience watches her different parts light up as she explains their functions.

You are impressed with the overall plan of this most complex machine, the human body. You silently determine to take better care of your God-given, once-to-be-lived-in body-house!

> I will praise thee;
>   for I am fearfully and wonderfully made:
> marvellous are thy works;
>   and that my soul knoweth right well.
> PSALM 139:14

Because fingerprints of babies under five months of

age are unsatisfactory, footprints of newborn babies are made in many hospitals. As long ago as the 1500's footprints were used for identification in China.

Some pupils in my Health and Physical Fitness class found it hard to believe that just one foot could hold twenty-six bones. When all of these bones are squeezed into tight or poorly fitting shoes, the natural line of the big toe is often changed, thus crowding the other toes.

Incorrectly fitting shoes can cause painful corns, calluses, ingrown nails and enlarged joints. It is a startling and sad fact that the feet of civilized men are usually very badly cared for. Twice as many men during World War II were rejected for foot problems than for dental problems.

"My feet are killing me!" complained the attractive secretary, slipping her offenders out of her pumps and wiggling her nyloned toes under her desk. Feet are often accused of being lethal, but I have yet to read that cause in an obituary.

Shoes are surreptitiously (or otherwise) removed at school desks, at concerts, during films and lectures, on public conveyances, and in the privacy of our own homes. From American pre-schoolers to their great-grandparents, there seems to be a quiet movement "under foot" to free our feet from this confinement dictated by civilization.

The average woman walks over eight miles per day.

Your feet work hard for you. During your regular physical examination, be sure that your feet are examined, and given any necessary treatment by your doctor.

Some foot pampering points

1. *Keep them clean* (chapter 2 deals with baths but for now, just *feet*).

Wash your feet daily in warm water and mild soap.
Avoid hot water and harsh soaps. The sole of the feet has
more perspiration glands than any other equal area of
the body. They must be kept clean.

If you have calluses, soap them and gently rub them
with a wet pumice.

Rinse well.

2. *After the bath*

Dry your feet thoroughly (between the toes, gently).
Rub in lanolin, olive oil, body oil, or a baby oil to restore
the surface oils.

A light dusting of body or deodorant powder feels good.
(No deodorant powder on hand? Make one, by thoroughly
mixing together equal parts of talcum powder and baking
soda.)

A witch hazel application has a cooling, restful effect.

3. *Your pedicure*

The best time for this is right after your bath.

It is, with a few exceptions, like your manicure.

Cut the nails *straight* across. Rounding them, as in
fingernails, can promote ingrown toenails. Buy a good
toenail scissors from a cutlery shop.

Your nails should be cut to the same length as your
toes, or a little shorter.

Use an emery board to smooth the edges (a kindness
to your hosiery, too).

Cuticle treatment: gently push back the cuticle with
a cotton-tipped orange stick which has been dipped into
either olive oil or a commercial cuticle remover. *Do not
cut the cuticle!*

If you use nail polish, separate your toes with wads of
cotton while applying the polish and while it dries.

Decide what day of the week is best for your schedule, and then adhere closely to a weekly pedicure.

Potpourri

Never cut corns or calluses.

If a nail corner is slightly irritating the skin, ease a little cotton under the nail corner, using an orange stick.

Place a little lamb's wool over any slightly inflammed spot on your toe. Lamb's wool can be found at your drug store — it is packaged like a small roll of cotton.

Talcum powder sprinkled in your shoes will add to your foot comfort. (Don't be concerned about your stockings. It washes out.)

When shopping for new shoes, have both feet measured, and have the new shoes fitted to the longer foot.

Wear stockings that are long enough for your feet. If they extend one-half inch or so beyond your big toe, your foot will have the freedom it requires. Stockings, like shoes which are too short on the feet, can cause bunions or other foot discomforts.

Make a change of shoes during your day. Wear play shoes for play, work shoes for work, and heels for evening and other dress occasions.

Use a rubber or other soft mat in front of the sink or any place where you must stand for any length of time.

Elevating your feet for fifteen minutes leaves you feeling rested and relaxed.

<hr/>

"My feet are clay all the way up to my armpits," is one of the provocative lines from *For Pete's Sake*, a film produced by the World Wide Pictures and featuring a guest appearance by Billy Graham.

Ten Fingers, Ten Toes

Echoes and Overtones

Yes, the body has many parts, not just one part.

If the foot says, "I am not a part of the body because I am not a hand," that does not make it any less a part of the body.

And what would you think if you heard an ear say, "I am not part of the body because I am only an ear, and not an eye?" Would that make it any less a part of the body?

Suppose the whole body were an eye — then how would you hear? Or if your whole body were just one big ear, how could you smell anything?

But that isn't the way God has made us. He has made many parts for our bodies and has put each part just where He wants it.

What a strange thing a body would be if it had only one part!

So He has made many parts, but still there is only one body.

The eye can never say to the hand, "I don't need you." The head can't say to the feet, "I don't need you."

And some of the parts that seem weakest and least important are really the most necessary.

Yes, we are especially glad to have some parts that seem rather odd! And we carefully protect from the eyes of others those parts that should not be seen.

While of course the parts that may be seen do not require this special care. So God has put the body together in such a way that extra honor and care are given to those parts that might otherwise seem less important.

This makes for happiness among the parts, so that the parts have the same care for each other that they do for themselves.

If any part suffers, all the parts suffer with it, and if one part is honored, all the parts are glad.

Now here is what I am trying to say: all of you together are the one body of Christ and each one of you is a separate and necessary part of it.

I Corinthians 12:14-27 *(Living Letters)*

❧

Who shall ascend into the hill of the Lord?
And who shall stand in his holy place?
He who has clean hands and a pure heart . . .
Psalm 24:3,4 (rsv)

❧

Whatever your hand finds to do, do it with your might . . .
Ecclesiastes 9:10 (rsv)

❧

Thy word is a lamp to my feet,
and a light to my path.
Psalm 119:105 (rsv)

5

Your Hair, a Halo

Hair that shines with cleanliness and good health is like a beautiful magnet on one's head. When worn in a simple, becoming way it is sure to attract many admiring glances.

Stringy, oily, or unkempt hair, on the other hand (or, more specifically, *on another's head*) is a natural repellent!

Granted, you don't want to have tattle-tale-gray underwear, a chipped finger nail, or a wax-filled ear. But you could walk around with these liabilities without too many people being aware of them. Hair, however, is much too obvious to try to hide or to "think away." It is on us like a neon light for everyone to see — unless it is cowering (?) under a wig. (Considering buying a wig? Wait until you can invest in a very good one.)

Be proud of the appearance of your hair. Capitalize on your magnetized halo! You need never be ashamed of your hair, if you employ the following basic steps for its care.

There need be no "credibility gap" in your home hair

care, except for one item — that of cutting or shaping it. This calls for a professional — one who wets your hair and uses a razor.

A good cut, based on 1) your type of hair, 2) your facial features, and 3) your overall body proportions, is the essential base of every good hair style. It will help your home setting fall into place naturally and last longer.

Cutting is one step which neither you nor any well-intentioned friend can do for you. I wish it were possible to undo the cuts (?) I've given myself and a few others. So do they! And so do the beauticians, who had to start with an enigma rather than from scratch!

Brush . . . Brush . . . Brush

Reasons for brushing

1. Brushing helps the health of the hair by stimulating the scalp.

The *root* of the hair is that part under the skin. The *shaft* is that part which we see, the free end. As we brush our hair, the scalp is massaged. This stimulates the action of the oil glands which open into the hair roots and it also brings more blood to the scalp. Blood supplies the oxygen and food needed by the new hair cells, all of which start in the *follicles,* the base of the hair roots.

2. Brushing distributes the natural hair oils over the entire length of the hair shaft.

3. It gives the hair natural sheen and beauty.

4. Brushing removes dust and lint particles, excess oil, and skin scales.

5. It makes the hair more manageable.

6. Brushing removes dead hair. The life expectancy of any human hair is from a few months up to four years. When the old hairs fall out, they are replaced by new

ones. Doesn't that remind you of an oak tree, whose dead leaves hang on tenaciously all during the winter, but, in the spring, give way to new, healthy leaves? Rather than being concerned about hair found in your brush be thankful to be rid of the old dead hairs and just comb them out of your brush.

Who should brush

People with dry, oily, thick, thin, curly, or straight hair. Yes, *everyone*, regardless of the condition or type of her hair, should brush it.

If your hair is too oily, you might understandably reason that brushing is not for you. True, it will seem to bring out even more oil at first. But while you are brushing, the oil glands of your scalp are being stimulated and before too long should be behaving normally. Stick with your daily brushings and prove to your own satisfaction that the oil flow will eventually level off.

Another help for oily hair is to wrap a clean, dry piece of cheesecloth, an old nylon stocking or some absorbent cotton around your brush, allowing the bristles to come through. Now brush your hair. This method helps absorb the extra oil and also the dust particles which the oil attracts and holds.

Another pointer for those of you with oily hair, is to cut down (or out) on butter and fatty foods and eat more green, leafy vegetables and drink more water.

The type of brush to use

A convex, natural boar bristle brush is the best. It is also the most expensive. But it is worth the extra cost, because is does much good and no harm, and will last for years.

Wire brushes may scratch the scalp and break or pull

out some hair. Some other brushes are not effective enough in promoting circulation.

Cleanliness of brush

Always use a clean brush, even if this means washing it out every night, though usually, washing it after every shampoo is sufficient.

Wash your brush and combs in a mild dish detergent in warm water. Rinse and dry (preferably in the sun) with the brush bristles *down* (so as not to become water-logged).

It is a good idea to own two brushes, so that a clean, dry one is always available. Unhealthy hair and scalp conditions can be contagious. Use only your own brush and comb.

Your position during brushing

The following positions will induce even more blood to the surface of your scalp:

If *standing,* bend over from your hips so that your head is hanging low.

If *sitting,* spread your knees apart and drop your head down between them.

If *lying down,* let your head hang down over the side of the bed. You may lie either on your back or on your stomach, just so you keep your head hanging low over the side.

Method of brushing

Take a firm grip on your brush handle.

Start at the nape of the neck and brush through the entire length of the hair with one rolling motion of your wrist and convex brush. Would you like that in slow motion? O.K.

Place the back of the brush against the back of your neck. Now, revolve the brush until you feel the bristles. Start brushing, and continue to revolve the brush along the entire length of your hair.

In other words, you start each stroke with the bristles on one side of your brush and finish with the bristles on the opposite side. Clear?

Continue brushing vigorously like this, all around your head, in the opposite direction to which your hair grows.

Amount of brushing

If this vigorous brushing is new to your head, limit it to about 25 strokes at a time. Increase this daily until you are consistently doing at least one to two hundred strokes per day.

Some girls, enthusiastic about what one hundred strokes have accomplished for the beauty and manageability of their hair, have increased it to four and five hundred strokes per day, with shining results.

Time for brushing

Twice daily (morning and evening) is more effective than once daily. Don't feel limited to these two above-mentioned times.

We associate brushing our *teeth* with the time directly following eating and before retiring. Do you know any-one who programs extra tooth-brushing sessions in between these customary times?

Hair brushing is an entirely different thing. Brush at odd intervals between your regular brushings. Take advantage of telephone, television, and record-listening time by brushing! True, your head will not be hanging down (except perhaps for the last) but your hair will benefit from this extra brushing.

Brush back through your hair when you first remove curlers. No, it will not hurt your set.

If you use a spray on your hair, you will have to give special attention to brushing in order to combat dulling of your hair.

Give it a vigorous brushing before every shampoo.

Brush it again (with a clean brush) after the shampoo.

Brushing is even more important in winter than in summer because the extremes in temperature affect one's scalp and tend to make the hair dull.

At a demonstration program, we had some girls sing the following ditty, while Melanie (with beautiful, glossy hair) stood before the audience and demonstrated with her brush.

This Is the Way We Brush Our Hair

(Demonstrate brushing hair correctly by bending over and enthusiastically brushing)

This is the way we brush our hair,
Brush our hair, brush our hair.
This is the way we brush our hair,
With one hundred strokes a day.

We hang our heads down very low,
Very low, very low.
We hang our heads down very low,
For one hundred strokes a day.

Now our hair will glisten and shine,
Glisten and shine, glisten and shine.
Now our hair will glisten and shine,
With one hundred strokes a day.

(Demonstrator stands erect, pauses for audience reaction to her bright red face and to her hair "on end," and then proceeds to brush hair into place)

> We brush our hair right into place,
> Into place, into place.
> We brush our hair right into place,
> After one hundred strokes a day.

Shampoos

When to shampoo

1. Before your hair actually looks like it needs it. (In other words, as often as is necessary to have your hair stay fresh looking and fresh smelling.)

2. Once a week is enough for the average head of hair. Granted, there are exceptions.

I'm reminded of a lady, around whom we children were ill at ease, because to us she looked austere (probably she wasn't at all). This rural lady, who lived with no concept of today's air-pollution problem, had soft white hair, which she arranged neatly on top of her head. She claimed the distinction of shampooing her hair once each summer. The other 364 days she merely brushed it out.

I understand that even now there are some ladies who perform this washing "ritual" only every few months.

But, shampoo we must, because there is no magic formula!

3. If your hair is excessively oily, you will want to wash it every three to five days, or perhaps, daily. Or you might choose to alternate with dry shampoo.

4. Shampoo after swimming in salt water.

5. After swimming in a pool with chlorinated water.

6. Thursday night, or Friday during the day are the prime weekly time slots, because this prepares you for the weekend.

Where to shampoo

I must admit that this sounds elemental. But I'm listing

these different places chosen by some of my friends to prove that there need be no monotony. In fact, it could be rather like going from one beauty parlor to another within your own home, but always to the same beautician, unless your roommate, friend, or relative offers to spell you.

... under the shower
... in the bathtub
... in the bathroom washbowl
... in the kitchen sink
... in the laundry tub
... in a basin

(Note: All, except for under the shower, require a spray attachment, a sprinkling can, or a big pitcher for rinsing.)

Types of shampoos

1. According to hair type. Purchasing a commercial shampoo is no problem. Just choose one right for your hair condition, normal, oily, or dry (as labeled). Take your preference as to cream or liquid shampoo.

2. Soaps that make effective shampoos . . .

... Pine Tar Soap. During my first job, I worked with a lady who had long, lustrous black hair which she wore becomingly in a French braid.

When I asked Mrs. Rosenburg her secret for such beautiful glossy hair, she modestly replied that any credit belonged to her mother who had brushed her hair daily as a child and who had always shampooed it with Pine Tar Soap. You can buy it in drug stores.

... Plain brown laundry soap. Astonished? So was I. But a beautiful, fastidious friend of mine insists that no shampoo can compete with plain brown bar soap from the laundry department of grocery stores.

If you could see Gay Nell you would stock up on brown bar soap!

... Any gentle dish detergent.

... Any mild bar soap can be used as a shampoo. But don't rub the bar itself on your hair. (This applies to Pine Tar and brown bar, also). Instead, do one of the following:

    a. Make a lively suds of the soap in hot water, and then shampoo with the suds.

    b. Shave bits of the soap into hot water, leaving it to dissolve. Make enough of this "shampoo" to last several weeks.

  3. Dry shampoos. If you have a cold, an illness, or for some other reason cannot wash your hair, it still will look presentable after a dry shampoo. If you don't have a commercial one use cornmeal. You merely:

Apply the dry shampoo to your head.

Rub it in thoroughly.

Wait a short time.

Brush it all out with your brush covered with cheesecloth. As you brush out the dry shampoo, you will also be brushing out the oil which has been absorbed and the dust and dirt from your hair. Doubt it? Look at your cheesecloth!

  4. Egg shampoo. This is a fun thing to do at home, and gives added sheen to the hair.

Beat the whites of two eggs.

Beat the yolks of these eggs.

Fold the beaten whites into the beaten yolks.

Soak your hair with lukewarm water.

Apply about half of the egg mixture and massage it well into your hair.

Rinse well with *cool* water. (Remind yourself of what

happens to eggs left on the egg-beaters when the beaters are dropped into *hot* water, and you won't wonder why we stress *cool* water for this step. Cooked eggs are good on a plate!)

Apply the rest of the egg mixture and massage it in thoroughly.

Rinse well with *cool* water. Next, rinse with warm water, and last with cool water.

Now, *feel, look at,* and *smell* your hair! Lovely!

Preparation for a regular shampoo

Collect all necessary supplies:

good absorbent bath towel;

a wet washcloth or small towel for accidental soap in eyes;

hair brush;

shampoo;

rinse (optional. But lemon juice diluted in warm water is good for blondes and red heads and vinegar diluted in warm water is equally good for brunettes. Or you may choose a commercial rinse. There's no dearth of them on the market).

Brush your hair vigorously.

Appoint someone else to answer the telephone, or else just let it ring.

Giving the shampoo

Soak your hair thoroughly with warm water.

Apply the shampoo; rub it in well throughout your whole head.

Massage your head vigorously with the balls (not the nails) of your fingers, covering thoroughly every smidgen of your scalp. (Having a beautician silently carve my scalp with her nails while she gaily chatters on is one of my pet peeves.)

Rinse out all of this shampoo with warm water.

Repeat the shampoo and rinse steps.

Rinse and rinse some more, until your hair squeaks.

If you're using vinegar (or some other rinse) apply that now.

Rinse again.

Your head and hair are clean, squeakingly and beautifully clean. Don't you love the smell of a clean, wet head? That, for my money, is one aroma that would be well worth bottling!

After the shampoo

Clean up your shampoo area and put each item in its correct place. Wait! Are the caps and covers screwed on tightly?

Drying the hair. The best situation is to be lounging in the privacy of your own back yard, while you leisurely brush your hair dry in the sunshine. Obviously, this prime time is limited, especially to Northerners.

If time is no factor, and you cannot be outdoors in the sunshine, there is no reason why you should not just brush your hair and allow it to dry at room temperature.

Home hair dryers work faster than either of the above methods. But use the *warm,* not the *hot* position on the dial. The latter can be too drying for your hair and for your complexion.

Apply a moisturizing cream to your face before using the hair dryer. Remove the dryer as soon as your hair is dry.

Styling Your Hair

As your eyebrows are the frames for your eyes, so your hair is the frame for your face.

Skin your hair back tightly from your face and completely cover it with a towel or scarf tied in the back. Now, look in the mirror and appraise the shape of your face. Is it long, triangular, square, round, oval, or heart-shaped? It will be one or some combination of these basic shapes.

Continue to scrutinize your face. Common sense and honest thinking will now help you decide how to wear your hair. If your face is long, you will vote against a long, straight hairdo; if round, you will choose to add height at the middle of your head and to keep the hair close in at the sides of your head; if square or triangular, you will not want your hair flat on the top; if oval (fortunate you!) play up this natural beauty asset by avoiding a "busy," distracting hairdo. If you are petite, you would look top-heavy with an exaggerated bouffant style.

In other words, study what to do to emphasize your good features while detracting from your weaker points.

Straight hair can be very smart. Rub a little creamy hair lotion between your hands and then, while your hair is still damp, rub your palms over your hair. Like that lustre? Some of you with straight hair may still want a little more "body" as given by rollers, so read on.

Hair "hardware" (rollers and clips) is functional but certainly not aesthetic. Wear a becoming boudoir cap or wrap a length of pretty netting around your head while your set is in the making. This is a thoughtful gesture to the rest of your family or your roommates, and is also good for your own morale. It is an especially considerate wife who, when possible, does her hair while her husband is at work.

The fact that you see other women driving their cars or shopping in the supermarkets with heads full of curlers

gives you no license to do the same! Avoid it like the
plague! Leave the shopping cart at the supermarket and
your curlers at home!

Setting Your Hair

If your hair tends to have some natural wave, brush
it and coax the waves the way they naturally want to
go. Secure the waves and pin curls with clips. A style
based on the hair's natural lines looks best and is the
easiest to manage.

Those with curly or straight hair will probably want
to use rollers.

Use of rollers

Divide your hair into equal sections with your comb.

Pick up an individual hair section; comb it smoothly
in the direction opposite from which it will be wound;
hold it tightly as you place the roller at the very end
and start rolling. Roll it in the direction you want it
to go when combed out.

The larger the roller, the smoother will be the finished
look. Use smallest rollers or hair clips at the temples and
neckline.

Use of pin curls

Good for temple or neckline hair, or for bangs.

Comb each strand out carefully; work from the roots,
winding in a neat circle right through the tips. Make
clockwise curls for hair to be combed forward and
counterclockwise curls for off-the-face hairdos.

Use hair clips rather than bobby pins for regular pin
curls and cellophane tape for large, loose curls against
your cheeks.

After a dry shampoo

Set your hair in rollers.

Spray lightly with a quick-setting lotion (cologne is good for oily hair)

Between shampoos

If you like so many roll your hair each night, it is not necessary to dampen the hair. Just comb each section neatly and roll it dry.

Combing Out the Set

Brush your hair back from the forehead and sides with long determined strokes. This will not hurt your set. Now brush and comb it into place.

If you have short curly hair, a toothbrush makes a good hairbrush. This mini-hairbrush is also convenient to carry in your purse. (Your toothbrush for teeth will be in its case, so you won't be confusing the two in your purse).

Don't make a fetish of teasing your hair. However, it is good to know the mechanics of teasing in case your set shows some separation or you want some fullness here or there. At this trouble spot, hold your hair at right angles to the scalp with one hand while you gently back-comb some of this hair towards the scalp. Drop that hair section and now smoothly comb the top hair over it.

If you feel you *must* spray your hair, do it as lightly and as infrequently as possible. Keep that natural look!

We are being warned lately against an increasing number of eye injuries from household sprays. Particles from hair, deodorant, and other household sprays are smaller than dust specks and can become imbedded in the cornea of the eye. They may not be noticed at first, but cause irritation several days later. Usually this will clear up in a week or so, but some particles if deeply imbedded may cause permanent discoloration. Some· patients who had to discontinue wearing their contact lenses because of the pain, were able to wear them again after they stopped using sprays and the injuries had healed.

"In the case of hair spray," said Dr. Angus L. MacLean, of Johns Hopkins' Wilmer Institute in Baltimore, "it is easy to see how a user may become the innocent victim of damage to the eyes from marginal particles while the main body of the jet is being directed to the hair" *(Chicago Tribune)*.

Permanents

Permanents give body to one's hair and help keep a set longer. Home permanents can be safely given, if prefaced with a professional hair cut. Try to draft a friend or your husband (he's not your friend?) to help, especially in rolling the back hair.

If you have naturally wavy hair, you already have the best part of a permanent. Don't stoop to the canned variety. JoAnn has very thick, wavy hair. Its lustre shows that she brushes it. She tells of the "bush woman" period, when she had her one and only commercial permanent.

Color Touch-Ups

To tint or not to tint . . .

That is the question!

A prominent lady being interviewed on T.V. recently told of having given away all of her lovely light beige dresses when she decided to go "gray." At first she was glad to be rid of the nuisance of keeping up the hair color, but later she disliked her "gray" feelings and thoughts. Now that she has returned to color again (in her case, it is red), she feels happier and more like her true self.

Others who stayed or have returned to gray delight in wearing colors, are proud of their gray hair, and even highlight it. They feel that the gray hair is more flattering to their present skin coloring. Gray hair can highlight the rest of your beauty, as it does for Kay, Deln, Ginny, Eleanor, Lydia and Betty.

But whatever you decide, have it either/or, not both! The gray line is one line that knows no retreat, only camouflage. It's a "tattle-tale" gray which quickly answers the question, "Does she or doesn't she?"

A gray fringe at the top of brown, black or red hair has no more fringe benefits than does a dark fringe on top of bleach-blonde hair.

In *A Gift From the Sea,* Anne Morrow Lindbergh wrote concerning her solitary vacation in a "bare sea-shell of a cottage":

> The unfinished beams in the roof are veiled by cobwebs.
> They are lovely, I think, gazing up at them with new eyes;
> they soften the hard lines of the rafters as grey hairs soften
> the lines on a middle-aged face. I no longer pull out grey
> hairs or sweep down cobwebs.[1]

[1] Copyright © 1955 by Anne Morrow Lindbergh. Quoted by permission of Random House, Inc.

Your Hair, a Halo

Echoes and Overtones

A fine head of hair adds beauty to a good face.
PLUTARCH

❧❧❧

Tresses, that wear
Jewels, but to declare
How much themselves more precious are.
RICHARD CRASHAW

❧❧❧

Thy fair hair my heart enchained.
SIR PHILIP SIDNEY

❧❧❧

Are not two sparrows sold for a farthing? and one of them shall not fall on the ground without your Father. But the very hairs of your head are numbered. Fear ye not therefore, ye are of more value than many sparrows. Whosoever therefore shall confess me before men, him will I confess also before my Father which is in heaven. But whosoever shall deny me before men, him will I also deny before my Father which is in heaven.
MATTHEW 10:29-33

6

P-s-s-s-t!
Your Shoes Are Showing!

> How beautiful upon the mountains
>   are the feet of him who brings good tidings,
> who publishes peace.
>
> ISAIAH 52:7 (RSV)

Edith's feet have been doing just that for thirty years.

We saw her last spring, radiant in her mountain environment, and looking but scarcely older than the number of years she had been serving there.

We had exchanged occasional letters and Christmas cards through the years, but somehow I was unprepared for the stark beauty of this place. Here the mountains are so close that they almost squeeze the valleys out of existence, here sunsets are never seen, and only one-tenth of one per cent of the land is level (and that figure includes the creek beds). The fragrance of wild flowers and ferns comes to you undiluted, no filtering through city smoke or haze. And winding through all of this natural beauty is the everpresent mountain stream, straddled here and there by picturesque swinging bridges.

We accepted Edith's invitation to go for a ride to see

some of the grade schools where she and her associates teach Bible, and to see the homes and meet some of the people who attend their Mission Chapel.

We had not anticipated that we would be leaving the road, but leave the road we did!

My car-loving husband sat in the front seat enjoying this supreme experience, while our daughters and I were in the back. I was thankful for them and the car to hold onto.

This demonstration ride was over unexcelled proving grounds, across bumpy creek beds — splashing right through the water. We turned around in small spots and shot up and down mountain terrain at rakish angles. While my husband was marveling at the performance of the four-wheel drive, the short wheel base and the high wheels, the girls and I were comparing this experience to a mad combination of a roller coaster, whip, and some non-patented rides.

After reeling out of this International Scout to a firm footing in front of the peaceful little Mission home, I began to almost enjoy our Appalachian ride — in retrospect.

As Edith was serving dinner that evening, I was admiring her hands. They are nicely shaped with graceful fingers, strong, well-manicured nails and prominent half moons.

But it was her *feet* which took Edith to this Appalachian Mountain spot twenty-five years before a highway was put through there. And the residents of that mountain area whom we met that day plainly showed their love and respect for "L'il Ole Miz Shaw" whose "beautiful feet" brought and continued to bring them "good tidings."

In succeeding chapters we will be investigating specific

things to do and to avoid doing with our feet. But first, we will concentrate on their 1) appearance and 2) care.

From the standpoint of the wall mirror, we have two general views: 1) with shoes and 2) without shoes. In this chapter we will deal with the appearance and the care of our *shoes*. We discussed the appearance and care of our *feet* in chapter 4.

Let's start by glancing back into the history and evolution of shoes as recorded in the encyclopedias.[1]

The Evolution of Shoes

In Bible times, homemade sandals protected feet from rough stones and hot sand. People living in cold climates protected their feet by homemade moccasins — bag-like coverings tied on with strings.

If any of today's styles seem "way out" to you, compare them with some of the shoes from previous centuries, and they will seem mild!

The rank of wealth of the early Greeks, Romans, and Egyptians was announced by their shoes. Long pointed toes and unusual decorations indicated high rank. The 14th century featured a shoe whose pointed toe was so long that a chain was required to hold it up in order for its wearer to walk.

During Queen Elizabeth's reign, the *duckbill* shoe reached such wide proportions that a law was passed restricting its width to five and one-half inches. (Really!)

The *chopine* was a wooden shoe with an iron ring for helping the wearer lift his foot from the mud.

[1] The information that follows was taken from *The Encyclopedia Americana*, 1966 edition, and from *The World Book Encyclopedia*, 1967 edition. The information on shoe lasts can be found in *The Story of Lasts*, National Shoe Manufacturers Association, and in *How Modern Shoes Are Made*, United Shoe Machinery Corporation.

The *jack boot* with a large cuff-like top was worn by gentlemen and soldiers from about 1650 to 1775. A wearer could not remove these boots unaided because of their tight fit and heavy weight.

Some ladies' heels of the 17th century were so high that the shoes had to be removed before the ladies could tackle stairs. (By the way, aren't you glad that the lower heels rather than spikes are the in-thing now?)

Men, not to be outdone by the fairer sex, also started wearing heels.

The short, well-known "Louis heel" was named after Louis XIV (1638-1715), who ruled France for 72 years. He was dubbed "The Sun King" because of his love for dazzle and splendor.

***

So, shoes of one type or another have been worn for many centuries, but not until 1850 (just prior to the Civil War) was there such a thing as a "right shoe" or a "left shoe." Previously both shoes were made from the same last.

Does this mean that George Washington, the Father of our country, never, in spite of his position and wealth, owned a right shoe or a left shoe?

Just think, Napoleon must have gained the coveted distinction of being Emperor of France and the greatest military genius of his day, without benefit of a right shoe or a left shoe!

This little nugget of information could be the basis for a popular song. Something like . . .

> With-out a right shoe, left shoe,
> Ei-ther shoe'd do,
> Yes, either shoe'd do . . .

It reminds me of a housekeeper who used to wear flats with a single buttoned strap. Each week she rotated her shoes so the soles would wear out evenly. It was a fun thing for us children to predict if the buttons would be on the inside or the outside.

Queen Victoria stirs my imagination the most! She was the ruling monarch of Great Britain (1837 to 1901) during the time of this startling innovation on the shoe market. Even without the help of television commercials to spark her interest, I'm relatively sure that. the idea of right shoes and left shoes must have appealed to the feminine instincts of the thirty-one-year-old monarch. But, don't you agree that she was probably discreet in her Victorian purchasing?

Recently while visiting the Stephenson County Historical Museum in Freeport, Illinois, I was happily surprised to have Mr. and Mrs. J. Carroll Moerk, the resident curators, unearth a carton of old shoe lasts. These had all been dated and the oldest ones were symmetrical. We took some pictures of them and of some ladies' shoes which obviously had both been made from just one last.

❦

The first American shoemaker was Thomas Beard, who came to Salem, Massachusetts in 1629. In the early Colonial days, cobblers used to travel from house to house making shoes for the different members of each family. They accepted board and lodging as part of their pay.

The General Court of the Bay Colony (according to *The Encyclopedia Americana*) forbade the wearing of extravagant styles in footwear by persons of "mean estate."

The 19th century was a golden era in the shoe industry. Shoemakers worked in "ten footers," little ten foot square shops nestled close to their own homes. They often read or visited with friends as they worked.

Many shops had a Bible in evidence.

Shoemakers in larger shops often sang together.

President Jefferson was criticized when he first donned pantaloons and lace shoes.

In pioneer towns, it was not uncommon for a thrifty farmer and his family to walk barefooted to town, carrying their shoes in their hands. They would stop at the edge of town to put on their shoes, and then walk in them to church.

In shoemaking families, the father's old boots would be cut apart and made over into shoes for the children.

It was the World War II period which saw the introduction of plastics, fabrics, and synthetic materials, partly due to the wartime shortage of leather.

⧓

Speaking of leather, have you ever smelled a tannery? One of my early childhood "smell" memories is that of the tannery in a neighboring town. We children, impressed with the reputed opulence of the owner, found it hard to reconcile his economic stature with the plain, old-fashioned "stink" of his tannery.

Last night, I entered a Chop Suey store with, "Um-m-m, it smells good here!"

The personable young Chinese salesman smiled, "Oh? I guess I don't notice it. You know how it is. I'm just used to it."

His unawareness of the tantalizing aroma did not signify a lack of appreciation for his culinary products. Rather, his sense of smell, once having become accustomed to that particular aroma, had become tired. The sense of smell, you will remember, tires more quickly than any of the other senses. Aren't you thankful that sight, taste, touch and hearing don't gradually "tune out"?

But back to the tannery, not to its odor but to its product — leather. Leather, according to my shoe salesman and shoe repairman, is still the most popular and the most healthful material for making shoes.

The Peacock

Now, girls, for a little change of position, let's walk over to the wall mirror to appraise the general appearance of the shoes or house slippers we are now wearing. Are they as clean and neat as they might be? Scrutinize them from all sides, with as much personal detachment as possible. Don't be embarrassed if they don't meet high standards right now.

Let's meet right back here for a few easy-to-follow time-savers.

Some of the astounding wealth and splendor of King Solomon is summed up in II Chronicles 9:13-28. Verse 21 reads, "For the king's ships went to Tarshish . . . bringing gold, and silver, ivory, and apes, and *peacocks*."

This refers to the period around 960 B.C. Though we do not know if "proud as a peacock" was an adage then, we are aware that peacocks were considered a great treasure and were carried to different parts of the ancient world.

Pliny, a first-century Roman writer, mentions the culinary delicacy of roast peacock served in its own feathers. Tsk! Tsk! Makes a little roast pig served with red apple in mouth, cranberries in eye sockets, and laurel wreath around neck seem almost commonplace!

It would be difficult to imagine anything more strikingly beautiful than the brilliant fan-like spread of the peacock, especially when bright sunlight plays on the metallic greenish and purplish blues. His stance is majestic!

What a cold-hearted observer, indeed, who would be unimpressed as the peacock struts before his "lady-love" — a drab-colored peahen, but attractive to him!

Were this gorgeous bird able to assess himself in a wall mirror, think what a start his *feet* would give him! How incongruous those ludicrous feet are compared to the ravishing beauty and the delicate texture of his feathers. From the mundane to the aesthetic in one quick glance.

The admonishment, "Remember the peacock" has an entirely different analogy than the more familiar "as proud as a peacock."

"Remember the peacock" was a favorite warning of Aunt Mag to my cousin Margaret. I pass it on now to you. Your wall mirror is a friend. Appreciate the help it will always be in alerting you to any peacock incongruities. Achieving an immaculate appearance merely from the ankles up, while disregarding unkempt shoes is to forget the peacock. Can you imagine coordinating a couture-designed gown with a pair of rummage-sale shoes?

Shoes should be neat, not just for the favorable impression you will make on others, but as a self-engendered morale booster for yourself.

The first stretchy-thing in the "it-can't-be-here-yet" morning, to ease your feet into a pair of neat, polished shoes, provides a psychological morning shot that no scuffed-up slippers or tired-looking shoes could possibly simulate. It is like the contrast of a bright, cheerful morning to a dreary, ominous one.

This pampering of yourself in consistently wearing neat

shoes reaps benefits for the other members of your family and for all others on whose wide screen your shoes appear every day in living color.

Do poorly cared for shoes completing an otherwise neat outfit remind you of the irrationality of applying fresh make-up to a soiled face or perfume to a body obviously in need of a bath and deodorant?

Finish the picture!

A fellow art student always started his paintings by boldly signing his name in the lower right hand corner of his blank canvass. His premature signature, glaring out like a blue ribbon, was apparently his inspiration for projecting a finished painting.

At a recent visit to an Art Gallery, some modern paintings featuring large canvasses painted somewhat solidly in single colors reminded me of that student's Solid White period . . . between signature and painting.

But he had a worthwhile lesson to teach us. If we start from the bottom of our "picture" with immaculate shoes, we can work from them to the completion of a neat, worthwhile composite picture.

For one generation to look askance at the succeeding generation's footwear is "nothing new under the sun." Fortunately, the popularity of dirty saddle shoes died with my childhood. Some mothers could wish that clean saddle shoes, rather than non-supporting loafers and sweaty tennis shoes, were the in-thing now. Can't you imagine one of your descendants of the mid-2000's chuckling over the present nylons and tennis shoe combination?

I'm now sitting under a dryer with a typical cross section of suburban footgear jutting out at me from beneath magazines and neighboring dryers. There are shined pumps, matted suedes, run-over loafers, polished oxfords, and nicked toes. (Mind you, I'm looking only at the *shoes,* and am in no way connecting them with the faces or with individuals. This would be hitting "below the belt." Besides, if my shoes are shined it's probably because of you girls who have been reminding me lately of these particular things.)

The several ladies who signed their pictures *first* this morning are the happier, I'm sure, as they leave here now. (It could well be that some of these were free from the early A.M. responsibilities of some of the others, whose pictures were not signed!)

The poor peacock is helpless to do anything to enhance the appearance of his personal foundation, but we are not! And speaking of the birds, let's not emulate the fabled ostrich by hiding our heads against shoddy foot attire.

Our County Shoe Repair man has been in business here for over forty years. The back of his pick-up tags reads:

> Wherever you go . . . whatever you do,
> Your shoes talk about you!
> Shoe repairing keeps them
> Looking like new!

And it does, together with the supplementary help of consistent home care!

"Eight out of ten people passing this window need new heels," says a window sign in the Esquire Shoe Repairing on East Adams, Chicago.

Home Care of Specific Shoes

Leather shoes

1. Keep them clean. Saddle soap is excellent for cleaning leather. Because this is a lubricant, it will also prevent the leather from drying and cracking. Our shoe repair

man sells a brand from England.

Warning: Saddle soap works so well that you will be cleaning all your leather shoes, purses, belts, and luggage and you will *glow* with satisfaction!

2. Use a reputable brand of *shoe polish.* Apply with any soft cloth. Polish with a regular polishing cloth. The shoe should be on the foot to do this well.

Suede shoes

1. The main thing is to keep them well brushed. A suede brush or a rubber sponge will remove loose dirt, and will help to keep them looking new.

2. A silicone spray can be purchased to prevent the suede from matting and to discourage water spotting.

3. Shiny spots can often be removed by rubbing gently with very fine sandpaper.

Gym shoes

Put them in your washer along with your other clothes.

Patent leather shoes

1. Spray with a reputable furniture polish. (I just learned this trick at a shoeshine shop.) Excellent for patent leather bags and belts, too.

2. Or, clean with "Vaseline." Both the polish and the "Vaseline" remove spots and dust and help prevent cracking, because they are both lubricants.

How to Ward off Your Shoes' Obituaries

1. Keep them clean and polished. This preserves their lives and enhances their appearance.

2. Clean them *before* putting them in the closet. If it's very late, and you're just too tired to brush those suede shoes or to wipe the scuff marks off your leather shoes, then leave them out in your bedroom. You will

see them in the morning, and can then clean or polish them before putting them in the closet.

3. Use shoe trees. They help retain the shape of the shoes, and also help prevent cracking.

4. Keep your S.O.S. (Save Our Shoes) box in your closet. It should include each necessary cleaning item for all the current shoes in your wardrobe. (Sort out items that are not relative to your present shoes and store them someplace in a well-labeled box. They might be useful at some other season.)

A drop cloth of plastic, cloth, or paper can be folded and kept with your S.O.S. box to prevent any accidents on your carpeting.

5. Check your shoes frequently. Take them to the repair man *before* they obviously need new heel lifts and other repairs.

6. Keep your laces clean and neat. White and other light-colored laces perk up beautifully when washed. Replace bedraggled-looking laces with a new pair. It's a small investment that pays big dividends.

7. If your leather shoes get wet:

    a. Stuff them with wadded-up newspaper.

    b. Place them away from direct heat.

    c. Allow them to dry slowly.

    d. When completely dry, wash and lubricate them with saddle soap.

    e. Give them a thorough shoeshine.

    f. They will look no worse for having been soaked!

8. Keep your shoes neatly in the closet. Keep them in shoe bags, in labeled shoe boxes, in see-through shoe boxes, on shoe bars, or in neat rows on a shelf.

Shoes that you are not wearing this season could be put in a labeled box in storage.

This review has hit home with me, but I've really enjoyed going at my shoes! I have taken two pairs to the repair shop, have bought one pair of fresh laces and three new pairs of pink shoe trees, and have transferred my S.O.S. material from a cardboard shoe box to a metal box (a Polish ham container). Some recent camera advertising included a colored picture of a peacock. You guessed it — that is now on my S.O.S. box!

If you're not satisfied with your present S.O.S. box, why not look around your home and come up with something different? Perhaps you'll come across a basket you are not using or you might like this metal box idea.

It's a good idea to buy your first pair of heels (even the new lower heels) a couple of weeks before appearing in them. Practice walking in them at home until you are accustomed to the different feeling (the shortened step, and the different body alignment) and can walk confidently and with good posture.

In just a few minutes, we'll be through with this discussion. Then you may all disperse to your own closets, remove all of the shoes there, take a good close look at each pair, decide what, if anything, should be done to each shoe and then *do it!*

P-s-s-s-t! Your Shoes Are Showing!

Echoes and Overtones

Let's close this chapter with the verse which started it. For matters of practical purposes, shall we substitute some other areas for that of the "mountains" mentioned?

How beautiful, *in the neighborhood*, are the feet of him who brings good tidings . . . who publishes peace.

How beautiful, *in the school*, are the feet of him who brings good tidings . . . who publishes peace.

How beautiful, *in the office*, are the feet of him who brings good tidings . . . who publishes peace.

How beautiful, *in the church*, are the feet of him who brings good tidings . . . who publishes peace.

How beautiful, *in the home*, are the feet of him who brings good tidings . . . who publishes peace!

Prayer

Lord, make me an instrument of Thy peace;
Where there is hatred, let me sow love;
Where there is doubt, faith;
Where there is despair, hope;
Where there is darkness, light;
Where there is sadness, joy.

O Divine Master,
Grant that I may not so much seek to be
    consoled, as to console;
To be understood, as to understand;
To be loved, as to love;
For it is in giving that we receive;
It is in pardoning that we are pardoned;
And it is in dying that we are born to eternal
    life.

SAINT FRANCIS OF ASSISI

7

You Are Being Framed!

You are an artist!

Oh yes you are.

You are aware of *lines*. That is why you arrange your books and magazines in that certain way, place a chair just so, comb your hair this way, then that way, and set your table to look just right to you.

You react to *colors* — in your home, on other people, in magazines and in nature.

It's fascinating to watch a professional picture framer at work, choosing the frame and then the matting with much thought, placing the picture with precision, just so.

It is this "personalized picture framing" which you do several times each day, as you dress for work, sports, dinner, church or parties. Yes, your clothes are the frame for *you*, the picture. As your eyebrows frame your eyes and your hair frames your face, so your clothes frame YOU.

The art of beautiful dressing is simplicity. Dress modestly and conservatively. Keep the colors beneath your personality, of which your clothing is an expression. Keep *you* more noticeable than your clothing.

Owning a few clothes which are correct for you is preferable to an excess supply of unsuitable garments.

Foundation Garments

The importance to any outfit of a good basic foundation is obvious. In order for your foundation garments to perform adequately for you, they must be carefully chosen. Consult a licensed fitter in her own little shop or in the underwear department of a larger store. In the privacy of a fitting room you will be measured and given professional advice regarding the type and make of undergarments best suited to you.

Once you have had this service, you will be forever spoiled for the shop-to-shop, wonder-which-and-why type of underwear buying. If you have steered away from this service thinking it was only for the overweight, I can understand. So did I, for years! This free service is for you, if you are a "Twiggy," a 36"-24"-36", a 40"-40"-40", or any other combination.

Incidentally, the accepted ideal figure proportions are for the bust and hips to measure the same and the waist to measure at least ten inches smaller. Diet and exercise will help you attain this.

This book is not a book on diet or exercise, but there is a wealth of such material at your book store or library. Here, we will just say that regardless of your weight or proportions, the most important thing for you to remember is to maintain good posture.

Among other things, the fitting specialist can teach anyone who doesn't know, *how to put on a bra:*

Slip into it so that the straps are on your shoulders.

Bend over from your waist to allow all tissues to fall into position.

Now stand up straight as you finish fastening bra.

She can also teach you *how to put on a girdle:*

Fold the top of it over (outside) toward the bottom.

Step into it and pull it up over your hips.

Now, unroll the top up to your waistline.

To remove your girdle, just reverse these three steps.

Tailored white slips, cut straight across the back, are the best type. Choose the right length for you. Wear a black slip with a black dress.

Having acquired the garments correct for you, the next responsibility will be to keep them clean and in good condition. To have them look better, smell fresher, and last longer, stockings and panties should be washed after each wearing. Other underwear should be washed frequently.

The many excellent products on the market (nylon bleach, fabric softeners, and cold water soaps) make this a pleasant little chore.

❦

The following idea is the result of a time and motion study relative to underwear identification. We have been spending too much time sorting and identifying our own undies from the family wash. If there are three feminine members in your family, that means at least 21 pairs of pants per week. Perhaps you would like to try our solution:

1. Choose a different color marking pen for each feminine member of your household.

2. Fill in a rectangle of your color, at least $\frac{1}{4}''$ x $\frac{1}{2}''$, on the labels of your slips, bras, girdles, blouses and

pajamas. Use the same identifying mark on the soles of
your socks and the upper part of your hosiery. Mark
your panties on the outside of the waistband, both mid-
front and mid-back. Fold them lengthwise in thirds and
then crosswise in half. So, even when folded, they will
announce their ownership.

This little effort has revolutionized our laundry detail.
Now anyone can quickly sort the clothes into accurate
piles, and each owner is responsible for folding, mending,
and ironing her own clothes. This identification not only
shows up more clearly than name tags but has the added
advantages of requiring less time and effort to apply and
of costing less.

ɪᴄᴀᴀᴀ

Treat your clean underwear and yourself to well-
organized dresser drawers. Would you like to line your
drawers? Choose from perfumed and flowered drawer
lining, gift wrapping paper, adhesive-backed paper, or a
pretty colored foil.

Underwear folded in neat piles acts as a time-saver and
a morale-booster. Decide just where each pile belongs, and
keep it there, so that you would be able to find an article
in the dark with no rummaging around. You will want a
pile just for slips, another just for nighties or p.j.'s.

It was Kate Saunders, a blind lady, who alerted me as
a thirteen-year-old. to the disheveled condition of my own
dresser drawers by showing a friend and me how she could
locate any article of her clothing. (I must admit that
there have been times since when my dresser drawers required at least partial sight and other times when my 20-20
vision was somewhat inadequate.)

You might like my "tops and bottoms" idea. I chose

this natural order for the same reason that one says "bacon and eggs" rather than "eggs and bacon." Because "tops" come first and we are left-to-right oriented in our reading and thinking, I have the bra pile to my left and the panties pile to the right of it. For the same reason, sweaters come before shorts or slacks, and in the closet, blouses are hanging up to my left of the skirts. "Tops-Bottoms!" Easy?

Either in your closet or a dresser drawer, have a workable sewing kit including scissors, needles, thread (black, white, plus the main colors of your wardrobe). Safety pins? Forget them!

How about decorating an empty cigar box for this? (These discarded boxes are given away in drug stores, restaurants, and other places where cigars are sold.)

Your jewelry is scattered here and there? This, too, could be organized in a cigar box or two.

How about camouflaging your sewing and jewelry boxes with pretty coverings — cloth, pictures, paint, or adhesive paper? Wooden boxes are best. If yours is a cardboard box, why not glue on a raised button for the handle?

Your Clothes That Show

While shopping for a winter coat, I overheard this bit of conversation between the members of a family who were buying the grandmother a coat.

"But that coat just doesn't do anything for Grandma!" complained one of them.

"Just what is it that you want the coat to do for her, anyway?" retorted another.

A thoughtful question and one deserving a thoughtful answer. Just what is it that *you* want your clothes to do for *you?*

Fit

Your clothes should look as if they belonged to you, as if tailor-made. They should fit closely and trimly, but not tightly.

Have you read *With Malice Toward Some* by Margaret Halsey? I remember her impression, while at a social function in England, of being at a party where everyone had exchanged outfits, so poorly did their clothes fit.

Colors

The colors should harmonize with your own coloring or should flatter you by emphasizing some good feature.

Your eyes are a pretty shade of blue? Play them up by featuring that identical shade in your clothing.

Our church visitor and greeter is a charming lady who wears lush, lively shades of pinks and other members of the red family. They provide a striking complement for her silver-gray hair. A rather important part of that special Sunday A.M. "feel' is missing on the rare occasions when Mrs. Neale is not in our church foyer.

Borrow an idea from modeling schools to help you decide which colors are good for you! Collect samples (material, scarfs, crepe paper, or different articles of clothing) of all the different colors and shades you can find. Take these to a mirror where you can see yourself in a good light.

Now, take one color and drape it across the front of you from shoulder to shoulder so that no other color shows against your face. Study your own reflection. Is this color too loud, too dominating for you? Is it a color which makes you look dull or drab? Does it add spark to your appearance? Does it highlight your own natural coloring? Do you feel comfortable in it? Would you prefer it as a basic color or just as an accent?

Repeat this routine with each of the other colors, being as objective as possible in your answers.

The colors will form themselves into distinct piles, the Never-Wear and the Good-for-Me.

It's amazing what varying responses the same color will elicit from different complexions and hair colors.

Attractive, clothes-conscious Betty Jo, who can wear practically any color (and do justice to it) claims that if she wears black, someone will invariably ask, "Don't you feel well today?"

Staple colors (black, navy, brown, dark gray) make you look thinner.

Neutral colors and pastels have little or no effect on size.

Intense colors (clear white, shocking pink, fire engine red) tend to enlarge.

The psychology of coloring

1. *Red*. Down through the ages red has been associated with the heat of the blood, either in anger or love. It is a very intense color and the hottest of all.

Stones — ruby, garnet, jasper, bloodstone, fire opal.

2. *Yellow*. Yellow is associated with sunshine in the pure state. It is sunny and bright, and symbolic of warmth and light.

Stones — topaz.

3. *Blue* is symbolic of dignity, sedateness, and even sadness. It is one of the coldest colors, very formal.

Stones — sapphire, zircon, turquoise.

4. *Orange* (combination of red and yellow) is symbolic of richness.

Stones — opal, coral.

5. *Purple* (combination of red and blue) possesses the

strength of red and the coolness of blue. Most people can wear it. Use it in scarfs, ties, and other accessories to bring out another color, e.g. gray.

Stones — amethyst.

6. *Green.* Symbolic of nature. Very cool and vigorous.

Stones — emerald, jade.

Lines

The lines of your clothes should be right for you. This means more than just the silhouette. It refers to trimming, stitching, collars and cuffs, seaming, welting, tucks, rows of buttons and lines in the fabric.

1. *Vertical lines* lengthen and slim the figure. For example, a row of buttons or a different color down the center front of a dress will draw one's eyes up and down at the center and away from the sides (but a *series* of vertical lines would negate this effect).

The vertical line is a friend to one who would like to weigh less and/or be taller. A one-piece, one-color dress or jumper with no horizontal break in the middle achieves this vertical line.

2. *Horizontal lines* work to decrease your height and to add width, because one's eyes follow that horizontal line across from east to west. Examples of horizontal line emphasis are suits, sweaters and skirts, belts and a different colored top and bottom.

This horizontal emphasis is good for the tall or the thin person.

3. *Diagonal lines* flatter most figures. They seem to emphasize feminine grace.

This knowledge of optical illusions in the lines of your

clothes can be of benefit to you all through your life.

The amount of money spent on your wardrobe is not the important thing. Rather, it is the thoughtfulness with which you choose the right colors and lines for yourself, and the subsequent care which you give these clothes.

Fabrics

Heavy, bulky woolens are broadening. Mohair is for the very slender. Small prints are for small figures, larger prints (but not *too* big) are for larger figures. Satins, brocades, and metallics broaden. Dull fabrics slenderize.

Appropriateness

Dress appropriately for your age, your personality, and for the occasion (sport clothes for sports, *not* for church).

Do you remember a *Saturday Evening Post* cover (several years ago) showing a wife sitting up in bed, modeling her new ornate Easter hat? Oblivious to the incongruity of her midnight "ensemble," the lady was admiring her reflection in her hand mirror while her husband viewed her through one sleepy, questioning eye.

Complete Closet Clean-Up!

Choose the right day (I prefer gray, rainy days for a project like this). School girls or working ladies will need a Saturday, a vacation day, or a long evening. But make it soon!

Set the mood.

Background music would help to make the task a pleasant one without taking your mind off your work. You will have to concentrate on *clothes.* You will be forced to make one little decision right after another. So, don't plan to use this time for T.V. or for memorizing anything.

Start from scratch by removing every single item from

your closet. Now, you can do a thorough vacuuming and cleaning job.

If there is no trimming on your shelf, this would be something to consider now. There's a variety of possibilities — adhesive-backed trim, wallpaper border, plastic shelf trim, velvet ribbon, upholstery trim, ball fringe, ruffling or artificial flowers.

Remember, nothing is to go back into that closet unless it really belongs there *now*. If you have outgrown something, or if it has outlived its usefulness to you, put it in the give-away pile. If it will not be worn this season, put it in a zippered bag at the back of your closet or in a well-labeled box on your top shelf or in the attic. Don't give closet space to any item which gives you no returns *now*.

Check each item of clothing before returning it to your closet. Does it need some sewing (seams, buttons, button holes, snaps, hooks and eyes or hems)? If so, put it on your mending pile and promise yourself not to return it to the closet until it is repaired.

A friend whose skies were cloudy because of marital problems tried to compensate by buying expensive hats. The labels in those hats were impressive, but the careless way they were tossed on top of each other on her closet shelf was not!

Hat storage can present a problem. I worked on a new idea one day, and then stood back to admire my closet shelf sporting hats on glass quart jar pedestals. Neat! Why hadn't I thought of that before?

Some days later, I reached for a hat and its Humpty-Dumpty-pedestal came crashing to the floor!

With my hats back in hat boxes, I again was faced with the problem of knowing which hat was in which box. So, I bought some 3″ x 5″ gummed labels, drew a picture of each hat, colored it and applied it to the outside of its respective box.

Now my hat shelf not only looks neat, but the hats are kept dust-free, I can quickly locate any hat and there will be no more broken glass to pick up! And all for just a few cents and a little art time.

Clothespins on a dress hanger can hold scarfs hanging lengthwise. There will be no rummaging around to find the right one, and they will not become wrinkled as when folded on a shelf or stuffed into a drawer.

Your shoe arrangement and your S.O.S. box were discussed in chapter 6.

Coats and suit coats need padded hangers. But you don't own any, and don't care to buy them right now? No problem! What about your discarded nylons? They could be wrapped around a hanger and then covered with material (cotton or satin, in a color harmonizing with your bedroom colors). Or you could use cotton batting for the foundation. They taught us in modeling school that these handmade hangers are actually better than those you buy because you can make them even fuller (more like a natural shoulder).

Covered hangers are good for dresses and blouses, too, because they protect against the garments' slipping. Be ingenious and make some. Agnes, my sister-in-law, gave us some which she had covered with yarn. They're pretty, work well, and emphasize the bedroom color scheme.

Hang each garment carefully on its hanger, so that the shoulder line is right (careless hanging can make a shambles of a careful pressing job). Point all of the hanger hooks in one direction, preferably away from you.

Arrange your clothes in order — for example, coats,

jackets, best dresses, casual dresses, blouses, skirts, and slacks. Neat?

Your closet is clean and tidy! Everything's right!

Besides your S.O.S. box and your sewing kit, you will need a good clothes brush. If you don't own one just for your closet, this is the time to buy it (either a bristle brush or a rubber sponge). Decide on one special place to hang it or to lay it down. Be your own good friend by insisting that no intruders (gloves, scarfs, or tissues) ever usurp that place. It must be reserved just for your brush. A spot remover could be kept right by it. A special little sweater brush can conveniently be kept in your sweater drawer.

Each of these little hints can keep you from pressing the panic button, when you're in a rush to keep an appointment.

It's pleasant to open your closet door to a refreshing light fragrance. Pomanders are sold in many gift shops. But have you ever made one? Insert whole cloves into either an orange or an apple until the fruit is completely covered. Tie a pretty ribbon around it, and hang it up in your closet.

An even simpler way is to dry some orange and lemon rinds and put them with some whole cloves into a container—cottage cheese or some similar cardboard or plastic container (not glass. Remember?). Cover it with netting or cheesecloth or punch holes in its own cover and present this little handmade gift to your closet! You've decided to paste some pretty paper or pictures around the outside of yours? That's the idea!

Do you wonder about a fragrance which you might wear? Choose your fragrance (if any) to suit you and your personality. Any fragrance should be used carefully and with discretion. It is worn to enhance your overall picture, not to mask unpleasant smells.

Do not wear a confusing mixture of fragrances — hair spray, deodorant, make-up, mouthwash, body powder and perfume each with its own strong, distinctive aroma.

Of perfume, toilet water and cologne, perfume contains the strongest concentration of scent and oil. Use it sparingly (on skin, not on clothes) behind knee, inside elbow, behind ear, on temple, or wrist. It should not touch cultured pearls.

Toilet water is the second strongest concentration and cologne is the weakest. Spray sachets are pleasant for lingerie and scarf drawers and do not hurt fabrics.

Have you ever tried a touch of cologne on your pillow before retiring? Sweet, sweet dreams! !

A little cotton ball dabbed with perfume can be tucked inside your bra for long-lasting sweetness.

Speaking of scents, the air around this picnic table, where I'm typing this, is heavy with the scent of mock oranges. Heady . . . but delightful!

ᖴᐧᕊᑐᐧᖴ

A favorite smelling rendezvous of mine is an early morning Pennsylvania kitchen where Peg and her sister Frieda serve home-ground and seasoned sausage with their homemade pancakes topped with home-churned butter and swimming in pure maple syrup boiled down from the sap of their own maple trees. The toast, made from their own homemade bread, is enhanced by those home-canned preserves and the fresh eggs from their own hen-house. The fruit? Fresh or home-canned, of course! The coffee cake? Home-baked and hot. The coffee? No, they don't grow their own, but its delicious aroma mixes beautifully with all the others, and that rich fresh cream makes it special. Just thinking about the Morris kitchen makes me feel like sniffing and gives me the pampered feeling of a satisfied gourmet.

❧❦❧

Do you especially like the clean, fresh smell of spring air? I do.

One early spring day, Dorothy, who looks like a professional model, but is actually a model professional social worker, invited me to ride out into the country with her just "to smell."

We were noticing the clouds scudding along in the bright blue sky as we turned off the main highway in search of real country roads. We found one — a narrow dirt road winding through pastures and woods.

This was so beautiful and alive compared to the office where we'd been cooped up all winter. Dorothy said, "Let's stop the car a minute, so we can really smell *spring*."

She stopped the car. We both inhaled deeply as she opened her door — to a garbage dump!

Potpourri

If you're a maxi-model, avoid wearing a mini-skirt.

No matter how "in" a style is, avoid it if it is not right for you.

Don't overdress or underdress.

Don't feel compelled to be the first or necessarily the last to wear a new style.

The sheath line is slenderizing.

If in doubt about the appropriateness of a piece of jewelry with a certain outfit, remove it. Keep jewelry down. Never wear jewelry on a print.

If your neck is short or one you don't care to feature, don't wear dangling earrings.

A V-shaped neckline or necklace is good for a round face; a shorter, wider effect flatters a narrow face.

Wear both gloves or carry both gloves. Do not wear one and carry the other. Gloves add to your costume and give hands a soft look. They should correspond with your shoes and bag. Beige gloves are permissible with a brown bag. Kid gloves are always smart and may be worn any time of the day the year around. The more formal the occasion, the longer should be the glove you wear. Keep two or three pairs of washable white gloves on hand.

A watch is always acceptable. You do not have to try to coordinate it to anything.

Big handbags, large plaids or checks, and bulky fabrics overpower a small person.

Before buying a hat, look at your complete picture in a full-length mirror.

Before buying a dress or skirt, sit down in it before the mirror in the dressing room.

A-line skirts are good for the plump figure, but large patch pockets, ruffles, plaids and polka dots are not. The A-line, softly flared, softens figures and helps to hide figure faults.

Avoid wearing prints until any complexion problems are cleared up.

The one-color princess style dress is excellent for one who prefers to look taller or thinner.

Full or pleated skirts emphasize full waistlines.

Turtlenecks do not flatter short-necked or full-busted girls.

High necklines, ruffles, gay prints and waistline emphasis help the thin girl. Her collarbones could be covered with a soft scarf.

Your basic wardrobe is your springboard to a variety of right combinations for you. Keep it down to two or three colors to allow for uncomplicated interchange of outfits and accessories.

A contrasting belt widens the waist.

Light stockings make legs appear larger; darker stockings diminish the size of the legs.

The hemline of your coat should cover the hemline of your dress.

Avoid design upon design.

Bolero-type jackets are not for the full-shouldered girl.

Sandals are not appropriate with tailored clothes.

Scarfs are important. Bright ones can add much to neckline interest. Try tying your head scarf at the side of your face or at the back of your neck rather than under the chin. Bright scarfs perk up plain suits. Wear plain scarfs with plaids and tweeds.

If your coat has a belt, remove the belt while the coat is hanging in the closet.

As a rule you don't wear a suit for dinner, unless it is a dressmaker type.

Bone or beige shoes make your whole outfit appear lighter.

The double-breasted effect is broadening. It is becoming to tall, slender girls.

To take attention away from your waist or bustline, wear a monochromatic color scheme, rather than contrasting colors.

Blonds look good in soft medium to dark colors. They should usually avoid very pale or extreme pastel shades.

Sloping shoulders are helped by set-in sleeves. Dolman

or raglan sleeves are good for square shoulders.

Roll-up sleeves are not flattering to heavy arms.

Avoid a short or contrasting colored coat if you are heavy.

From tip to toe, each item of wearing apparel should be clean and neat. Cold water soaps, detergents, spray starches, fabric softeners, steam irons and self-service cleaners almost defy one to have dirty or unkempt clothes.

Remember that once you are properly dressed, you need not be concerned about your own appearance so are free to concentrate on other people and things.

Some Calendar Guidelines

Wear white shoes (except silk) only between Memorial Day and Labor Day.

No suede shoes after Easter.

Patent leather shoes are acceptable the year around.

No velvet after February.

Straw hats may be worn from February to Labor Day but white straws should wait for Easter.

"My Room and I"

Inspired by other ladies' "... and I's" (*The Egg and I,* Betty MacDonald; *The King and I,* based on Margaret Landon's *Anna and the King of Siam*) wouldn't you like to write *My Room and I?*

Our varied lists (shopping, Christmas, things-to-do, and others) are essential in organizing our time and work. Now here's a new list to work on, "My Room and I." This list will cover your personal grooming and bedroom-cleaning details for one week.

Using a ruler, divide a piece of paper into 32 blocks by drawing seven horizontal lines, and three vertical lines. In the upper left hand block, write, "Days of the Week," and starting with "Sunday," fill in the rest of that far left column . . . one day to each block.

In the top sections of the next three rows write in order, "Morning," "Afternoon," "Evening." Now fill in each personal grooming point and other reminders (vacuum, dust, closet check-up, wash, iron, and others) in the appropriate spot.

Each calendar will be unique . . . one of a kind.

If your mornings are all the same, just fill in once and then use ditto marks. It might look something like this:

> Stretch in bed; pray
> Exercise
> Wash; baby oil; deodorant
> Lemon juice in cup hot water
> Make bed — tidy room
> Brush hair 100 strokes
> Dress
> Comb hair; lipstick
> Breakfast
> Brush teeth

꙰

This is your basic weekly schedule . . . but it will not be immune to illnesses or other emergencies. But having "My Room and I" should help promote order and happiness in your home and outside life.

You Are Being Framed!

Echoes and Overtones

Consider the lilies of the field, how they grow;
they toil not, neither do they spin:
And yet I say unto you,
That even Solomon in all his glory
was not arrayed like one of these.

MATTHEW 6:28,29

A thing of beauty is a joy forever:
Its loveliness increases; it will never
Pass into nothingness.

JOHN KEATS

She's adorned
Amply that in her husband's eye looks lovely, —
The truest mirror that an honest wife
Can see her beauty in.

JOHN TOBIN

The fashion of this world passeth away.

I CORINTHIANS 7:31

8

More Beautiful Than Beauty

Nothing but onions can do for other foods what onions can! No aroma can simulate that of sun-dried clothes, of home-baked bread, or of popcorn! Neither can any feeling exactly match that of accomplishment. The more accomplishments we chalk up, the happier and more productive our lives become.

It is the ecstasy of learning to write your own name, of finally swimming the length of the pool, of baking your first pie, of losing those ten extra pounds, of learning to knit!

Perhaps as a child you were forced to practice the piano. But as an adult, you play because you choose to. Or you may be one of the many adults who seldom even touches the piano except to dust it.

As a child you also learned to sit, stand, and walk. These, unlike piano playing, can never become optional. In fact, life forces us to spend all of our waking hours doing one of these three things. As long as they are mandatory, we might as well do them gracefully. So we will devote one chapter to each of these three aspects of visual poise — sitting, standing, walking.

There are many other situations which call for visual poise. We shall discuss some of the most important ones here.

Some physical weaknesses or deformities may make it impossible for you to follow every suggestion.

Pat Schulert, a wheel-chair friend, has such a radiant expression, interest in others, workable faith, and positive attitude, that I wish it were possible to have one thousand copies of her made to be distributed throughout the world.

Ascending Stairs

Stairways and ladies were meant for each other, especially open spiral staircases (with chiffon, candlelight, and soft music)!

1. Flex your knees (actually *bend* them) and keep them bent all the way up the stairs. Think of your knees and hips as being well lubricated.

2. Maintain good posture . . . head held high . . . think tall.

3. Pull with the front leg (pushing with your back leg would cause a bouncing effect).

4. Keep your feet parallel to each other and pointing straight ahead.

5. Place your foot right on the step, rather than having your heel dangle over the edge.

6. Touch the rail lightly, if you choose to, but don't grip it tightly.

7. Work for a smooth effect, with no bobbing of your head. (Imagine yourself riding up on a ski lift.)

8. Do not glance down at the steps, except when you

start and again when near the top and then lower just your eyes, not your head.

After practicing this until all the points come naturally to you, you could use just three main points to remind you of stair-climbing position:

1. Keep your *back perpendicular* to the steps.
2. Keep your *knees bent.*
3. Keep the top of your *head* moving in as *smooth* a line as the moving hand rail of an escalator (not like the jerky, angular lines of the stair steps).

∝

But, you live in a ranch house with no basement? So do we! And who's going to practice walking up and down a pull-down stairway to the attic crawl-space?

Don't despair!

Practice walking around your house with your knees bent (just like in a charm school). Exaggerate this position. Then when you are confronted with stairs, you won't feel so silly about bending your knees.

Thoughtfully practice on the stairs in stores, schools, churches, museums and other public buildings.

Now are you sure of yourself on stairs?

Then you're ready for a special treat!

Go to an escalator (one that is empty, or nearly so) and *walk* up it.

Yes, *walk* . . . don't just ride! This riding walk will give you a soaring sensation, if you're applying your new rules.

One more step?

Walk up a *fast* escalator (like the one leading to the observation floor of the Prudential Building in Chicago). This gives wings to your feet!

Anyone for a Mary Poppins umbrella?

Descending Stairs

1. Stand with good posture at the top of the stairs. Think tall!

2. Glance down (with *eyes* only, keeping head up) to determine length of stairs and height of steps.

3. Keep hand in a poised position, just above the rail, touching it occasionally if you care to.

4. Keep your feet parallel to each other.

5. It is graceful for a lady to have both feet pointing slightly to the right or to the left as she is descending stairs. (Our graceful feline friends come down stairs diagonally, too, you know. Another thing we can learn from cats is to stretch before getting up mornings.)

6. Keep your head movement smooth. Think of your head as moving parallel to the rail instead of to the steps.

7. Glancing down at the steps is necessary at first to determine the depth of the steps. Once this is established, it is not going to change, because steps are consistent. So don't glance down again . . . until toward the end, to insure your "landing" at the proper time.

Stepping Up and Down Curbs

Apply the same principles as for walking up and down stairs. Maintain good posture, flex your knees, and keep your movement smooth (no head bobbing or jerking).

Putting on Your Coat

An orderly way is easier than any haphazard way of putting on your coat, and looks much more graceful.

1. Hold the top of your coat in both hands with the lining side toward you. Have your thumbs in or pointing to the armholes and your fingers on the fabric side of the coat.

2. Let go with your right hand and put your right arm into the right sleeve.

3. Pull coat well onto your right shoulder with your left hand.

4. Reach your left hand back *(down,* not up) and put your left arm into the left sleeve. Do not look back, the armhole will be there. Pull the coat up on that shoulder.

5. Adjust the coat until you feel comfortable.

Isn't this fluid? It eliminates the possibility of putting your arm into the wrong sleeve, of having one arm with no sleeve available, or of slinging your coat over your head or shoulders boy-fashion.

Removing Your Coat

There are two acceptable ways of taking your coat off.
First way

1. If your coat is buttoned, start unbuttoning it at the top, slipping the bottom of the button out of the buttonhole, using just one hand.

2. Hold lapels with both hands and drop the coat slightly back off your shoulders.

3. Drop your arms and reach down behind you, catching both cuffs in the left hand. Tug gently until the coat is taken off the right arm.

4. Bring your left arm around to the front (both cuffs will still be in your left hand and your left arm will still be in its sleeve).

5. Take the edge of both sleeves in the right hand and pull, easing your left arm out of its sleeve.

6. Grasp the top of the coat in your left hand, fold it over your arm, hang it up, or lay it down.

Second way

Steps 1 and 2 like above.

3. Drop your arms and reach down behind you.

4. As the coat slides off, grasp the top of it with both hands at or near the arm holes.

5. Continue to hold coat with right hand as you slide your left hand over to the center back.

6. Grasp center back of coat with left hand.

7. Drop right hand.

8. Bring coat around to front with your left hand.

Your Gloves

Gloves are an important part of your outfit. As long as they must be put on and taken off so often in public, let's do it gracefully.

Hold your hand *up*, with fingers pointing *up*, when putting on your gloves.

Insert all four fingers first, smoothing on one finger at a time, and then insert the thumb. (Usually with cotton gloves, the whole hand can be inserted at one time).

Take your time at smoothing on your gloves.

When you remove your gloves, again hold your hands *up*, and ease the gloves off slowly — finger, by finger, by feminine finger!

Have both gloves *on* or both gloves *off* (do not wear one and carry the other). If you carry them, carry them lightly. Put them in your purse rather than clutching them tightly in your hand.

You may shake hands with your gloves on.

Picking Up an Object from the Floor

Picking up the morning paper from your front steps, helping your child with his shoelaces, dusting the bottom rungs of your chairs, and picking flowers share a common problem . . . how to stoop gracefully!

1. Walk up to the side of the object and stop with one foot ahead of the other.

2. Flex your knees and go down, using your leg muscles and bending at hip and knees, while keeping your back as straight as possible.

3. With graceful wrist motion, reach out the hand which is nearer the object, and pick it up.

4. Rise to your original position by using your leg muscles.

These are practical pointers which you will be using many times each day . . . not just when there is an audience.

Practice the right way to go down gracefully in front of your mirror. Now, watch yourself stoop over by keeping your knees stiff and bending over from your waist. One demonstration should be enough to convince you to never bend down *that* way.

Handing or Accepting an Object

Remember that the *profile* of your hand is especially graceful-looking. As you hand an object to someone, slowly extend your arm in a smooth, graceful manner, with palm facing *in* or *up* (not down). Look into the person's eyes and smile!

You will find these next steps helpful when accepting a cup of coffee from your neighbor, a gift from a friend, a special delivery letter, a graduation diploma, change at the cash register or a book from the librarian.

1. Look into the giver's eyes and smile.

2. Extend your arm slowly. With clockwise (for right hand) wrist motion, gracefully turn your hand over and up, keeping your fingers relaxed (slightly arched).

3. Give a pleasant, audible "Thank you."

Opening a Door and Closing It Behind You

Walk up to the door. Turn the knob and continue to hold it as you pull the door open.

As you walk through the doorway, gently pull the door after you (continue looking ahead, never back), and switch hands behind your back, so that the other hand catches the door knob and gently closes the door.

Perhaps this sounds complicated. But try it. The result looks effortless and uncluttered.

If you were to estimate the number of times you have to open and close doors during the course of just one week, you would value even more the ease of these simple steps.

Entering a Car

1. Face toward the front of the car, with your side toward the door you are entering.

2. Raise the foot that is nearest the door and place it a few inches inside the car.

3. Push up slightly with your foot that is still on the ground, shifting all of your weight to the foot inside the car.

4. (Simultaneously with number 3) Bend your head, lower your body to a sitting position (keeping your back straight).

5. Slide onto the seat.

6. Draw in your other foot.

7. Settle way back so that the back of the seat is supporting your whole spine.

If entering a low car, or if your skirt is too tight for the above steps, place your hand on the car door, slide your hips onto the seat and swing both of your feet in together, keeping knees and legs together!

Leaving a Car

1. Slide as close as possible to the door.
2. Swing out your foot that is nearer the door until it touches the ground.
3. Bend your head and twist your hips until you face the door.
4. Swing your foot from the car down to the ground by your other foot.
5. Walk gracefully away, thinking tall.

If leaving a low car, or if your skirt is too tight for the above steps, swing both legs around to the outside (keeping knees and legs close together) and down to the ground.

Exercises for Relaxing

You are applying for a position—you have an important telephone call to make — or are backstage, waiting to be announced — or your guests are just about to arrive — or, for some other reason you are excited!

The following exercises will help you relax. They require no props and can easily be done, whether you are standing or sitting.

1. Have your arms and hands loose at your sides. Keeping your hands relaxed, start shaking them vigorously, faster . . . harder . . . as if shaking the life right out of them. Feel them tingle? Then you are doing it correctly.
2. Blow out your lips . . . just like a horse! Granted, this sounds unrelated to relaxing, but, try it. It works, doesn't it?
3. Yawn. That's right! Just, plain . . . *yawn!*

More Beautiful Than Beauty

Echoes and Overtones

Grace is more beautiful than beauty.
RALPH WALDO EMERSON

❧✦☙

A lovely being, scarcely formed or molded,
A rose with all its sweetest leaves yet folded.
LORD BYRON

❧✦☙

Adorn yourself with all those graces and accomplishments, which without solidity are frivolous; but, without which solidity is to a great degree, useless.
LORD CHESTERFIELD

9

Your Head in the Clouds; Your Feet on the Ground

Have there been times when you have felt "all arms" or "all legs"? Have you ever wished that you could just unhinge them and park them in some unobtrusive place until after the party? I have!

This chapter starts with a promise to you . . . a promise that, after having studied the material and having practiced it many times both with and without your wall mirror, your appendages should never again cause you any undue self-consciousness.

Exaggerated claims? I think not.

You will be confident in all standing situations: while serving at a punch-bowl, standing for a snapshot, being in a reception line, at a party or a sport's event, while waiting at a bus stop, or just standing visiting with friends.

Because of our many varied activities each day, it is normal to think of our bodies as in motion. But of the three basic body positions involving no necessary motion — sitting, standing, and lying down — we do a surprising

134

amount of both sitting and standing during the course of any one day.

A motionless position might well indicate a very simple one to be slid into naturally and with no thought. As a matter of fact, this is too often the case with standing and sitting — resulting in unnecessary fatigue, in careless walking, and in a poor general appearance.

Poor posture is an enemy against which neither beautiful clothes nor a well-proportioned figure can successfully compete. While one carelessly sits or stands with no particular thought to the mechanics of it, poor posture immediately starts to father one or more of the following undesirable offspring: stooped shoulders, a spare tire, a protruding stomach, a dowager's hump, a sway back, backache, strain, or even spinal curvature.

Good posture helps to keep our body organs in their correct positions; it helps them do their work more efficiently. When we slump over, the organs of the chest incline to sag. The normal lung action may well be hindered, with a lowering of oxygen intake. The organs of the abdomen may sag, too. So correct posture is essential for good health, as well as for good looks.

Let's go directly from generalities to *you*. How is *your* posture? Happily enough, you won't have to ask anyone else, as there are simple ways to test your own posture. Also, there are some easy exercises to help develop and maintain good posture. Correct posture is of utmost importance, and the attention we give it should be stimulating rather than tedious and difficult.

Treat yourself to the luxurious, come-alive feeling of good posture. This is not a commodity which can be purchased for you by a loving husband or a doting mother. This is strictly a do-it-yourself project! Substitutes have been evolved for cream and sugar, but not for good posture. It has no substitutes! It did not in your grandmother's day, nor will it in your granddaughter's day.

Others may know the combination for your good posture, but, unlike opening a safe, only *you* can work this particular combination.

We enjoy watching the growth of families in our community. One family comes to mind now because all of them, from the father and mother right down to their tenth child, have excellent postures. (The father, Dr. Kenneth N. Taylor, is probably best known for having authored *Living Letters.)*

The good feeling that comes from good posture permeates the air and even makes others feel at ease and glad to be alive.

Now, are you ready for a quick boost to your self-confidence and poise? Do you want to look and feel more alert, more self-possessed?

It starts with good posture!

A Posture Checkup

1. Find a cord or ribbon about six feet long.

2. Secure a weight to one end of it. (I used the glass top of a discarded percolator, but a spoon, a heavy button, or any little weight would do).

3. Secure the free end of this ribbon to the top of your wall mirror (with masking tape on the mirror, or a thumb tack in the top of the wooden frame).

4. Hold a hand mirror in your left hand and stand with your right side toward the wall mirror.

5. Look at your reflection in the hand mirror and move until your ear is in line with the ribbon.

6. Now, assume your natural standing position.

7. Does the ribbon follow a straight line from your ear to your ankle, passing through the middle of your shoulder, the middle of your hips and the back of your knees? If so, you already have good body line-up.

More Posture Checkups

1. Stand with your back to the wall.

The parts of your body which should be touching the wall are head, shoulders, hips, calves, and heels.

2. Now, stand facing the wall.

Only your chest and toes should be touching the wall. Not your nose or your abdomen!

When a certain man, who lives in this house, unsuspectingly took this test, just *one* part (besides his toes) touched the wall. It was not his nose or chest! (And he insists that his waistline hasn't changed since World War II?)

❦

Even if you rated high on these posture checkups, please go through the following ten points repeatedly in front of your mirror (front view and side view). You will find it helpful to repeat the points aloud as you check these items from head to feet.

The Correct Posture Line-Up

1. Str-e-t-ch! Hold your *head high.*
2. *Ears* . . . above the shoulders (not forward or down like a turtle).
3. *Chin* . . . parallel to the floor (not up, giving a snobbish appearance; or down, suggesting dejection or embarrassment).
4. *Shoulders* . . . relaxed and down (not thrust back or up).

5. *Chest* . . . high.

6. *Abdomen* . . . flat. Pull it in as if walking sideways through a tight squeeze.

7. *Seat* . . . tucked under.

8. *Thumbs* . . . at side seams. This will bring your hands back to the sides as if they belong to you, rather than hanging awkwardly at the front like some large tags you'd neglected to remove from a new dress.

"Thumbs-at-side-seams" puts the final touch to a beautiful picture! That one little movement (*back* to side seams) does wonders for your overall picture, just as straightening a crooked picture on the wall improves the looks of the whole room.

If you ever have to be in a *line* of girls (perhaps singing) it would be a kindness to your group to pass on this one little point!

9. *Knees* . . . relaxed.

10. *Feet* . . . parallel, the arches slightly lifted and the weight resting on the center of the feet.

That's it!

Stand tall . . . think tall . . . be tall!

Good posture indicates, not arrogance or pride, but health and self-assurance.

Posture-Improving Exercises

Walking, biking, basketball, rowing and other activities which emphasize straight backs and chests held high are naturals for helping develop good posture.

Edge-of-door exercise

1. Stand with your back against the edge of a door.

2. Push your waistline against the door.

3. Push your neck back, and lift chest.

4. Raise arms straight up over your head, and push them back as far as you can.

5. Lower arms a little and again push back (several times).

6. Extend arms at shoulder level and push back (several times).

Wall-slide exercise

1. Stand with your back against a flat wall, with heels, seat and back touching wall.

2. Bend knees and slide down the wall, feeling the small of your back against the wall.

3. Return to standing position, continuing to feel small of back against the wall.

Floor exercise

1. Lie on your back on the floor, with your knees bent and feet flat on the floor.

2. Extend your arms out straight from your shoulders.

3. Inhale.

4. Contract your abdominal muscles.

5. Tip your pelvis up slightly, pushing the small of your back flat against the floor.

6. Hold while you count to five.

7. Exhale as you slowly straighten out your legs to the count of five, keeping the small of your back *down*.

␥

You have been working hard.

It's treat time!

For today's treat you will be given the master key to the secrets of standing with feminine grace and beauty.

This cannot be gift-wrapped for you, but it's yours for the reading and the application!

The Master Key

1. Start with the correct posture line-up. Imagine a strong, silk cord attached to the top of your head and pulling you straight up.

2. Now, imagine yourself standing on the face of a huge clock lying face up on the floor. Your feet are pointing straight ahead to twelve.

3. Point your right foot toward number one.

4. Place your weight on your right foot.

5. Draw the heel of your left foot up to the instep of your right foot (keeping weight on right foot).

6. Point toe of left foot toward number eleven on the imaginary clock.

❦

Now for a clue to help you remember your clock numbers:

Your right foot points to *one*. Think of this as being capitalized . . . *One*. Let it represent the One whose name "is above every name: that at the name of Jesus every knee should bow, of things in heaven, and things in earth, and things under the earth; and that every tongue should confess that Jesus Christ is Lord, to the glory of God the Father" (Philippians 2:9-11).

Your left foot points to eleven . . . why not to the faithful eleven of His original twelve followers? Then eleven could represent those faithful disciples plus the many thousands of other loyal believers up to the present time.

Now all of us, whether Jews or Gentiles, may come to God the Father with the Holy Spirit's help because of what Christ has done for us . . . *What a foundation you stand on now:* the apostles and the prophets; and the cornerstone of the building is Jesus Christ Himself!

Along with Christ, we who believe are carefully joined together as parts of a beautiful, constantly growing temple of God. And you also are joined in with Him and with each other by the Spirit, and are part of this dwelling place of God.

EPHESIANS 2:18, 20-22, *Living Letters*

With God's Son for our foundation and our sights fastened on Him and His followers, we will always be in good company, and can concentrate on these things rather than on ourselves.

About the master key? Well, while you stand in this position, you are assuming the stance which is most socially acceptable . . . *the model stance!*

Now, assume this model stance in front of the wall mirror. Don't you make a much prettier picture now than if your feet were to be parallel and pointing straight ahead? Move the knee of your left leg closer to (slightly in front of) your right knee. Is that a further improvement? It should be.

One final improvement: turn your imaginary clock so that *ten* rather than *twelve* is in direct line with your mirror. This means that you will have to move both of your feet to keep them in the *one* and *eleven* positions.

Ready?

Look in the mirror! Isn't that the quintessence of feminine charm and beauty? This position (just off dead center) is your most attractive. It also helps camouflage any leg irregularities.

Remember this position when anyone wants to take your picture. Keep your feet at *One* and *eleven,* but move your clock around!

Isn't it amazing what charm and femininity can be evoked by just a couple of little movements?

Good posture is a doorway to success. Maintain good posture to walk better, look better, feel better and to have more self-confidence.

Good posture is a matter of habit. It is a healthy mind in a healthy body. It represents an assured person who is interested in life and in people and looks upon them with awareness and expectancy.

Other positions for feet while standing

1. Reverse the position of your feet, having the left foot in back and bearing most of the weight, with heel of the right foot at the instep of the left.

2. Move the front foot ahead . . . leaving the body weight on the back foot or shifting it to the front foot.

3. Stand with your feet almost parallel and about one foot apart, with the toes pointing slightly out.

4. Stand on one foot with the ankles crossed and just the toe of the other foot touching the floor.

The hesitation stance

You have been walking and now have stopped (perhaps to answer the telephone), with one foot ahead of the other. Putting your weight on the foot in front, *slowly slide* the back foot (heel up, off floor) forward until its instep is at the heel of the front foot.

This is something no *man* would do. But it's so pretty on *you.*

Some Graceful Arm Positions While Standing

1. When your arms are hanging at the sides, keep your thumbs at the side seams, rather than having your hands

hang awkwardly at front. (But avoid this position with the above number 3 foot position.)

2. Cross your arms, by holding the upper arms lightly in your hands — thumbs under the arms and fingers lying gracefully on top.

3. If you put your hands in your pockets, have your thumbs on the outside of your pockets.

4. Both hands may be behind you: one, hanging limp just behind your hip and the other with the knuckles on your hip just behind the hip bone (elbow in line with shoulder).

5. Rest the back of one hand in the palm of the other in front of you, with all fingers facing up.

Rather than holding this position at dead center at your waistline, it is better to hold your hands just a little off center and just above or below your natural waistline.

Your Head in the Clouds; Your Feet on the Ground
Echoes and Overtones

Beauty without virtue is a flower without perfume.
A FRENCH PROVERB

Training is everything. The peach was once a bitter almond; cauliflower is nothing but cabbage with a college education.
MARK TWAIN

Be watchful, stand firm in your faith, be courageous, be strong.
I CORINTHIANS 16:13 (RSV)

Put on the whole armour of God, that ye may be able to stand against the wiles of the devil.
EPHESIANS 6:11

10

Please Be Seated, Ladies!

"Please be seated, ladies," is a simple directive with a wide range of possibilities. It could involve a straight chair, upholstered arm chair, school desk, rocking chair, sofa, counter stool, car seat, chaise lounge, piano bench, picnic table bench, ottoman, floor pillow, raised fireplace, step chair (as for ironing), train, bus or airplane seat, bleachers, theater seat, church pew, sailboat, rowboat, canoe, floor or lawn.

Can you imagine substituting "seat" for "rose" in Gertrude Stein's line "A rose is a rose is a rose"?

Negotiating this variety of seats in a fluid, graceful manner will require (1) know-how (which the next few pages will provide) and (2) practice (which you will be doing before your mirror).

But before we start, here is a promise! After today, you will have the *confidence* to accept any seat throughout the rest of your life, and the *ability* to sit on it gracefully.

Recently, a lovely soft-eyed mother said, "Just think
. . . I've been sitting all of my life, and never knew how
before. And it's really so simple, isn't it?"
Yes, it is simple.
You are anxious to start? So am I!
A straight chair in front of your mirror and a yardstick
(or something similar) are the only props you will need.

There are four basic steps in the sitting process: approaching the seat; seating yourself; sitting position; and
leaving the seat. We will study each of these in order.

I. *Approaching the Seat*
(Just read now . . . practice later)

Walk directly toward the chair, neither rushing nor
dawdling. Maintain good posture all the way. Did you
ever see a walking doll with a hunched back or with head
thrust forward? Never! Be a doll — a walking doll!

Don't obviously anticipate sitting by assuming a sitting
position while still walking. You have seen people, while
yet a distance from their chairs, lean over, bend their
knees and lead with their lowered heads. If this were a
game of charades, you might guess, "an airplane coming in
for a landing?" — "a horse straining under his load?" —
"an embarrassed ostrich?"

II. *Seating Yourself*

Now that you are standing tall by the chair, what should
you do?

A. The *general answers* are:

1. Glance down at chair (keeping head erect, but not
stiff) to make sure you are close enough to sit.

2. Pivot (raise heels and twist on toes) and lower yourself to the chair in one fluid motion, without looking at
chair (it will be there). As you lower yourself to the

chair, keep your hips tucked under firmly, your back straight, and your head held high. Use your thigh and hip muscles for lowering yourself. Do *not* use the arm of the chair for support.

3. Do not smooth your dress over your seat with your hand, as you sit down. If you feel you must smooth out your dress, just ease it out slightly at the side as you lower yourself to the chair.

An unpleasant combination occasionally seen along the church pew is the (1) "sitting-walk" *plus* the (2) hand-sliding-over-the-seat ritual.

Both of these are ineffectual: (1) Even if your head does proceed the rest of you, it is physically impossible for you to sit until your seat is in front of the spot where you will be sitting. So walk tall all along the pew, until actually ready to sit. (2) The hand-sliding accomplishes little except to outline your personal contours.

4. As you lower yourself, relax your arms to the front, turn both palms upward and lower them to your lap, one hand resting gracefully on the other as you sit.

5. As soon as you are seated, slide back as far as you can so that the chair back supports your whole spine.

B. The *specific answer* to "What should you do?" is that it depends upon how you approached your chair . . . from the front, the left, the right, or diagonally . . . or, whether you had just been standing in front of it.

Obviously, there are different ways to sit. We will give you just *one* way for each of these situations. Read each one through and then practice it. (Keep book in hand for reference, if you care to.)

Approaching a chair at your right

1. Walk as if you were going to walk right past the chair.

2. Stop when you are directly in front of the chair. Your feet, one ahead of the other, will be parallel to the chair.

3. Pivot and sit. Maintain good posture; don't lean forward.

   a. If your right foot is ahead when you stop walking, it will be your left foot which is ahead when you are seated. Isn't that smooth and graceful? Try it again!

   b. If your left foot is ahead when you stop walking, you will be crossing your legs (preferably below the knees) as you lower yourself to the chair. Your left foot will still be ahead when you are seated. (Feeling like an animated pretzel? When practiced enough this is very graceful looking).

Now approach the chair and sit down the way you used to. Don't you prefer the assurance and finesse of the new way?

Approaching a chair at your left

This is like approaching a chair at your right, only now you will be pivoting clockwise, and it will be your right foot which is ahead when you are seated.

Approaching a chair from the front

1. Walk up to the chair as if you were going to walk right through it.

2. When one foot is at the chair, pivot and sit, without looking back.

   a. *If your right foot is ahead at the chair:* A counterclockwise pivot will find your left foot ahead when seated. A clockwise pivot will seat you with your legs crossed above your knee (more difficult . . . but fun!).

b. *If your left foot is ahead at the chair:* A clockwise pivot will find you with legs crossed below knees and the right foot ahead. A counterclockwise pivot will find you with legs crossed above the knee and the right foot ahead.

Approaching a chair diagonally

This deserves the blue ribbon for femininity!

1. Arrange your steps so that the calf of your leg will touch the chair on your last step. If you're approaching from the right of the chair, it should be your left calf; if from the left of the chair, your right calf.

2. Pivot and sit as on the previous chair approaches.

3. You will be seated diagonally across the seat with your hips at a back corner and knees at the opposite front corner. (Many agree that this figure "S" is the epitome of feminine loveliness for sitting positions).

Sitting from standing in front of a chair

1. Feel the chair with the back of your leg.

2. Standing with one foot slightly ahead of the other, lower yourself to the chair, without looking back. Keep your back straight, and head high.

III. Sitting Positions

A. General posture

1. Sit tall (back straight, head high).
2. Chest up.
3. Tummy in and taut.

B. Regarding your legs

1. Center your hips on your two "sitting" bones.

2. Having the heel of one foot into the instep of the other looks graceful (the legs could be straight down or slightly to one side).

3. Crossing legs at knees should be reserved for thin legs, and then only when dress is not too short or tight. This position causes heavy legs to appear even heavier and thus more conspicuous.

Legs should not be crossed above knees at formal occasions or when you are seated on a platform (unless your part in a play should call for this).

If your legs are thin enough to be crossed, keep the upper leg hanging down straight; do not corkscrew it around the other leg.

4. Legs crossed below knees (with both feet on floor) look feminine. But do *not* thrust your feet forward resting them on the heels of your shoes.

5. Always *keep your knees together* when seated!

It's surprising how many times we see this rule broken — on high school and college bleachers, at neighborhood coffees and women's meetings, in restaurants, lobbies and terminals.

Regardless of your chronological age, please feel under obligation to yourself and to others to observe this rule *always* (except when playing a cello).

To help clinch this important feminine nicety, please sing and act out the following ditty in front of your mirror.

Knees Together
(Tune, *Three Blind Mice*)
Keep your knées tó-géther, knées tó-géther
(Feel them touching)
If it's hót or cóld or any kínd of wéather
Mén may sít with their knées a-párt;

(Spread knees apart mannishly)
But, lá-dies may né-ver — no, nó, bless your héart!
To in-súre a píc-ture of fém-inine gráce
Keep your knées tó-géther, knées tó-géther!
(Slide knees together again)

This distasteful picture (which Jennifer and Barb originally did for a program) should remind you not to inflict it on anyone else.

Try to make the impression indelible, so that from now on you will automatically be aware of your L.L.P. (Ladylike Position). Miss Sara and Miss Beulah, the two dear Smith ladies (one of them now blind) who coined that title many years ago, still thoughtfully exemplify this rule.

If that sweet little girl in Sir Joshua Reynolds' "Age of Innocence" were sitting on a chair, rather than on the ground, she might well have had her knees separated. Let's keep separated feminine knees confined to that tender naive age group which also sports baby teeth and chews gum in public! (Have you ever seen an expensively dressed woman whose slight jaw movements indicated a wad of gum? Never underestimate the power of one penny to obliterate the effect of hundreds of dollars.)

After a demonstration program, in which "Knees Together" was acted out, one of the girls' parents called us. This friend of long-standing, rather than starting the telephone conversation with the usual, "Hello, this is _____," lustily sang out, "Keep your knees together . . ."

But it required a bit of doing for this parent to explain his singing telegram to the wrong number he had dialed.

The *third* time he dialed, he reached our number. By this time he had retreated to the safety of, "Hello, this is _____."

His *second* dialing? Well . . . yes, he *did*. He dialed the same wrong number twice!

In a new Sunday school class of lovable seventh grade girls, I was faced with quite an array of sitting positions. One uninhibited little charmer even crossed her legs so that the ankle of one rested on the knee of the other. But that was the first Sunday. Soon they remembered — *knees together.*

We have discussed at length about keeping knees together, but if your knees were together and your feet sprawled apart, or your toes turned in, you would hardly qualify as charming. So, keep your feet close to each other (but not necessarily touching).

C. Regarding your back

1. Have your hips touching the back of the chair so that the chair back supports your whole spine. If the chair seat from front to back is longer than your thighs, then your back will be unsupported (but keep it straight), unless you choose to slide back and have your feet off the floor.

2. When leaning forward for any reason at all, bend from your *hips* (not your waist). This keeps your back in a straight line.

Have you ever seen a sitting doll affect a camel's hump? No! They have to keep their backs perfectly straight and bend only from the hips. Again, be a doll! A *sitting* doll. And Raggedy Ann (lovable though she is) is not a sitting doll.

According to my daughter's riding instructor, some teachers used to sew ramrods into the backs of their beginner's riding shirts to insure correct riding posture.

Place something gentler (a yardstick?) down the back of your dress. You may tilt it to avoid hitting the back of your head. Practice bending forward and to each side in front of your mirror. Good! A few more times. Now, remove the yardstick and "hump" yourself over lazily. Your mirror is a strictly truthful friend! When sitting, forget that your spine is flexible!

Bend From Your Hips
(Tune, *Three Blind Mice*)

Bend from your hips, bend from your hips
(Lean back and forth, back and forth with back straight)
Not from your waist, not from your waist *(hunch over)*
Lock up all your vertebrae *(sit tall and straight)*
If a doll can do it, so can you.
Bend from your hips, bend from your hips!
(Move correctly back and forth, back and forth)

But you're not going to be in a skit — so why should you practice this? You will need it many times a day for the rest of your life . . . as you sit at the dining room table, at your desk, at the sewing machine and ironing board and at coffees and teas. Your position does not remain constant at any of these or a multitude of other places. Remember, every time you lean forward, keep your back straight!

D. Regarding your hands

1. The general rule is to keep them together. (Exception . . . they may rest comfortably on your chair arms.)

2. One hand resting on the other (palms up or down) on your lap looks serene and graceful.

    a. If your *feet* are toward your *left,* rest your hands on the *right* side of your lap to balance the picture.

    b. If your feet are toward your *right,* rest your hands on the *left* side of your lap.

    c. Hold your hands still and unruffled. Superfluous motions (nail-biting, hair-fixing, unnecessary gestures accompanying conversation, smoothing out one's clothes, or nervously touching one's face) are distracting and put a blot on a potentially serene picture.

d. When reaching for anything (magazine, cup of tea, candy) lift your hand gracefully, and as you extend it, turn your hand (with fingers naturally arched, rather than sticking out straight ahead) until the palm of your hand is up.

e. Refrain from clasping your hands around your knees.

IV. *Leaving the Seat*

1. Have feet flat on floor, one ahead of the other.

2. Use your legs and thigh muscles to raise yourself from the chair. Do *not* use your hands on the chair arms or seat to hoist yourself up!

3. Maintain good posture (keep back straight, do not lean forward).

4. If you are in a low, or a long-slung chair, or any seat that proves a problem to leave, just slide toward the front of the chair (this is the *one* time that you may use the chair or the chair arms for support). Once having arrived at the front of the chair, drop your hands from the chair arms and rise properly.

5. Start walking away with the foot nearer your destination.

V. *Potpourri*

After diligent practice on a straight chair, you can graduate to overstuffed arm chairs and any of the other seats suggested at the beginning of this chapter. From now on, an unusual seat should be a pleasant challenge to you, rather than something to avoid.

Try a chaise-lounge

Picture yourself at a lawn party. The hostess directs you to a chaise-lounge. Rather than approaching it with a question mark almost visible above your head, and throwing one leg awkwardly over before attempting to sit, you walk up to it certainly, sit down gracefully on one side of it, and then, holding your legs closely together, wheel them up to a prone position in front of you.

Don't be surprised if you find yourself demonstrating these steps to your friends and family. Most people do! In fact, your demonstrations will help you remember the points even better.

To sit at a school desk

Imagine your straight chair as a school desk.

1. Stand, facing the front with your side next to the desk seat, and your feet, one slightly ahead of the other.
2. Gently lower and twist your body to the seat.
3. Keeping legs together, lift feet from floor and swing legs under desk.

To sit on the floor or lawn

Move chair away from mirror.

1. Stand with your left foot ahead of your right.
2. Bend both knees, until the right knee touches floor.
3. Slide left foot back, until left knee also is on floor.
4. Sit back on your heels.
5. Slide your seat to the left and your feet to the right, extending your toes.
6. You may sit with both hands on your lap or with one on the floor.

Practice these steps until they flow smoothly, one into the other, with no breaks.

To stand up from the floor or lawn

1. Lean forward a little as you manoeuvre to again sit on your heels.

2. Raise left knee, bringing left foot forward.

3. Put body weight on left foot.

4. Stand (using thigh muscles and maintaining a straight back . . . do not lean forward).

To sit on a theatre seat

Do not

1. look around at the raised seat, lower it and sit, *or*

2. stand with your back to the seat, lower yourself until you're sitting on the upraised seat, raise yourself enough to lower the seat, and then sit.

But do

stand with your back to the seat. As you lower yourself (maintaining good posture) have your hand back to feel the top of the upraised seat. Lower the seat with your hand as you continue to lower yourself. Sit.

The first two possibilities were put in here to further contrast their jumpy appearance with the smooth, co-ordinated way to do it correctly.

The following parody to "She's My Kind of Girl," was used as a demonstration. You will find it a fun thing to act out before your mirror. It is inserted here with the sincere hope that after seeing yourself in these various roles, you will always choose that of the last two lines. To read this is not enough, it must be acted out!

Sitting Pretty (?)

Some girls sit too stiff and taut
 (Exaggerated poker posture and straight, severe face)
While others carry marks of a battle fought.
 (Shoulders slumped, hands dangling and limp arms, head drooping forward and mouths, opened)

When girls fidget with their fingers,
   (Fix hair, pat face)
A vision of loveliness never lingers.
   (Chew fingernails or twiddle thunbs)
Toeing in or out
   (Toe in)
Will leave your audience in doubt.
   (Toe out)
A mannish pose is not for any girl who knows!
   *(Knees and feet greatly separated; arms folded across
   chest or hands on knees)*
Some girls kick with a frantic speed;
   (Legs crossed at knees; the upper leg kicking rythmically)
A solid football is what they need.
   (End with one big kick)
But, when one sits with a queenly calm,
   (Demonstrate. Oh yes you can!)
To her audience, she's beauty, peace, and balm.

❦

Please be seated, Ladies!

❦

Please Be Seated, Ladies!

Echoes and Overtones

Absence of grace and inharmonious movement and discord are nearly allied to ill words and ill nature, as grace and harmony are the sisters and images of goodness and virtue.

PLATO, *The Republic*

❧❧❧

Whatever she does, wherever she goes, grace orders her actions and follows her movements.

TIBULLUS, *De Sulpicia*

❧❧❧

A Seat to Avoid

Blessed is the man
   who walks not in the counsel of the wicked,
nor stands in the way of sinners,
nor sits in the seat of the scoffers;
but his delight is in the law of the Lord;
and on his law he meditates
   day and night.

PSALM 1:1, 2 (RSV)

❧❧❧

Their strength is to sit still.

ISAIAH 30:7

11

She Walks in Beauty

All the world's a stage,
And all the men and women merely players.
They have their exits and their entrances;
And one man in his time plays many parts,
His acts being seven ages. At first the infant,

.   .   .   .   .

And then the whining school-boy . . .
. . . Last scene of all,
Is second childishness . . . .

SHAKESPEARE, *As You Like It.*

"The baby can walk! ! "

Can anything compare with the child's look of accomplishment or with the mother's responding glow? The baby has been emancipated! She can put th-is foot a-head . . . now th-at fo-o-o . . ! She gets up and tries again.

The days of watching this progress are such happy ones, in spite of the fact that now many little goodies are accessible to the baby's reach.

Those first walking shoes are unbelievably soon supplanted by little girls' shoes. Now the feet can do more exciting things. They can hop, run, jump, slide and skip. With all of these alternatives, why spend time with unimaginative walking? That is for the dull . . . for the aged! No one is more acutely aware of children's aversion to walking than is the school teacher, who often reminds them, "No running in the halls!"

These free-spirited non-walkers eventually take one long slide into Teensville. Now, walking, which had become almost a lost art, is revived. But teenagers often find themselves harnessed with unbecoming walking habits. And who can criticize them? Their arms, feet, and legs seem too long and too numerous! Their fast growth rate promotes a rivalry between good posture and slouching. Besides, adults don't always provide the best examples.

The rediscovery of walking prompts the question, *"How should I walk?"*

This important question will be answered within the next few pages. You will have fun practicing and will discover that learning to walk by set rules supplants uncertainties with certainties, self-consciousness with self-confidence and as you know, self-confidence promotes self-forgetfulness.

Acting out the following lyrics before your mirror will further convince you of the necessity of a good, well-ordered walk. Spend considerable time imitating each of these ten ungainly walks. Don't underplay any of them. You don't know the melody? That's all right. Just say the words.

You're Not My Kind of Girl
(Tune, *She's My Kind of Girl*)

Some girls walk with a far-mer's stride;
Some girls sway from side to side;
Some girls lead right with their chins,

And that's where the trou-ble be-gins.
Toe-ing out is a dan-g'rous sport
If some-one's near, with whom to ca-vort;
Nor will toe-ing in your best friends win.
To my mind, you're not my kind of girl.
Minc-ing lit-tle steps can put your part-ner in dis-tress;
A spring-y lit-tle hop, for a charm-ing girl, is just a flop;
And slumps put you in the dumps;
Elbows stick-ing out could give one a clout;
A naugh-ty air will get you no-where;
To my mind, you're not my kind of girl.
(Second ending, to be sung at the end of this chapter)
But when you float along
Like a queen-ly song;
To my mind, you are my kind of girl!

❧

Surprising how many kinds of ungainly walks there are, isn't it? There are even more than the ten specific ones listed in the song.

Good posture is the basic requirement for correct walking. Since you have practiced correct standing and are aware of its importance, you are now ready to study the next step . . . walking.

What an Esther Williams can do for a dull-looking list of swimming rules, you will be able to do for this stereotyped list of walking rules.

Rules for Correct Walking

1. *Head* . . . held high, following a smooth line as you walk along (not bobbing up and down like a cork on choppy waters). My neighbor, Jane Sorenson, glides along as smoothly as if she were on a skate board.

2. *Shoulders* . . . down and relaxed, almost motionless.

It was a bright, lazy afternoon in a quiet village. A retired farmer and I were watching school children going home.

"Hey, see that girl a-comin' there?" he pointed. "I never see the likes of how she walks. I tell you that girl don't even walk . . . she jes' floats along."

Previously I'd have connected any interest in a girl's walk with either some women who were charm conscious or with younger men who might be attracted, not so much to the walk, as to the girl herself. Certainly this gentleman fit into neither of these categories.

His observation further alerted me to the importance of one's walk.

3. *Chest* . . . up.

4. *Arms* . . . kept close to body (not protruding out like fins), swinging easily from shoulders (rather than held rigidly like pokers at your sides). The swinging arc should be no longer than your step. Right arm and left foot are forward together and left arm and right foot are forward together.

Be sure that *both* arms are swinging naturally. It is not uncommon to see someone who swings one arm and keeps the other rigid.

5. *Hands* . . . relaxed at side, with palms facing inward not back, as in "rowing" yourself along.

6. *Abdomen* . . . in.

7. *Hips* . . . *still*, not swinging or swaying.

There were two fiddler crabs. The one was criticizing the other's walk.

"You sway so when you walk. Why don't you walk straight ahead? You would look much better!"

"Well," replied his amiable friend, "if you will show me what you mean, I'll try to imitate you."

A satisfactory demonstration never came off. As you know, a fiddler crab *must* sway from side to side as he walks. He has no alternative. But, you, a Homo sapiens, *can* walk straight, so don't cheapen your walk by imitating a Uca pugilator (fiddler crab).

Imagine yourself walking between two tightly-drawn silk chords (at hip height). These will hold your hips refusing them any east-west movement.

8. *Legs* . . . swinging from hips. Take short but not mincing steps. The length of your stride will be determined by the length of your legs, the height of your shoe heels, and the width of your skirt. Usually you think of a stride (distance between the two feet) as being no longer than the length of your foot.

9. *Knees* . . . relaxed (not tight or locked).

10. *Feet* . . . parallel to each other and about two inches apart. Start walking with the foot nearer your destination.

Reread this and think about these walking specifics. Memorize them and practice them repeatedly, one point at a time — with the mirror — without the mirror — and then back to the mirror again.

Sing the following ditty as you walk — in your home, to the library, or to the corner mailbox.

Lead With Your Thighs
Tune: *Bell-Bottom Trousers*
(Left foot down on italicized syllables)
Smo-oth, *smo*-oth, *as* you walk a-*long*;
Head high, *chest* high, *sing* this lit-tle *so*-ong!
Shoul-ders re-*laxed*, *tum*-my in and *tight*,
Lead with your *thi*-ighs, *now* you're walking *ri*-ight!

You do not learn to walk correctly until you are aware of your need. This awareness can be brought about in different ways: a member of your family may call attention to your poor walking habit, or your friends may, and their comments may not be as padded as you might wish. But the best way is for you to call your own attention to it.

You might be walking along downtown, and unexpectedly see an unattractive reflection in a store window.

"What a walk," you think. "Why doesn't she do something about herself?"

You do a double take!

"But, that's *my* dress . . . *my* hair!"

The truth penetrates. It is the plain, unvarnished *you* plowing along, with your head determined to beat the race.

So you decide to do something about it. You learn the mechanics of proper walking and you apply them.

The Living Walk

Once a lady has learned to walk gracefully, are we safe in assuming that her walking problems have been met and coped with?

Not really!

There are two distinct meanings to "walk." Dictionaries define walk:

1) to advance by alternate steps without running;

2) to behave, or to live.

Both of these walks, the *physical* and the *living* walks, have directions, restrictions, and promises!

The greatest Authority on our *living walk* had over 200 references to "feet" and over 350 references to the word "walk" put into His Book. The great majority of the latter refer to the living, rather than the physical walk; e.g., "For we walk by faith not by sight" (II Corinthians 5:7).

The Bible is a mirror to reflect our *living* walk.

We stressed the importance of correct stance before we could walk correctly physically. The following illustration from the Bible graphically demonstrates both the

Christian's stance and his walk. It is about someone who came face to face with his own reflection in God's sight. It was not pretty. He did something about it.

I'm copying this from the Bible my father gave Mother, with this inscription. "Merry Christmas, 1955. The best book to the best wife God ever gave a man." (The parenthetical inserts are mine.)

> I waited patiently for the Lord; and he inclined unto me, and heard my cry.
>   (God be merciful unto me, a sinner.)
> He brought me up also out of an horrible pit,
>   (the darkness of sin)
> out of the miry clay,
>   (One sin leads to another, and sucks us down, like quicksand, doesn't it?)
> and set my feet upon a rock,
>   (Jesus Christ, God's Son, the firmest foundation)
> and established my goings.
>   (He is the responsible, loving Guide of our "tour!")
> And He hath put a new song in my mouth, even praise unto our God; many shall see it, and fear (feel a holy respect), and shall trust in the Lord.
>
>   PSALM 40:1-3

I have chosen a special Bible verse for *you:*

Teenagers and career girls

Thou wilt shew me the path of life: in thy presence is fulness of joy; at thy right hand there are pleasures for evermore. — PSALM 16:11.

Wives and mothers

I will walk within my house with a perfect heart. — PSALM 101:2.

The life is imperfect, but the heart is "perfect" if sin has been confessed.

My mother's physical walk was not the best. She was inclined to toe out. But her Living Walk was an inspiration to people. A few years ago, just before she slipped into eternity, she whispered, "O Lord, it's so beautiful! Oh, thank You, Lord, thank You!" Her peaceful smile was so appropriate for one who had always lived close to her Lord.

My Mother walked within her house with a perfect heart.

Grandmothers and others of that age

With long life will I satisfy him, and shew him my salvation. — PSALM 91:16.

༺✦༻

Both the physical and living walks are often dealt with in the teenage group. It's as if a two-pronged walk responsibility were thrust at the teenagers with, "This is what you need," and, "Here is what you should do about it."

In other cases, neither the physical nor the living walk is straightened out until adulthood. Knowing the rules is not sufficient. They must be applied!

It is good to ask yourself *what* or *who* is your foundation. It could be one of several *things*: money, social stature, intellect, or position in life. Any of these foundations would be equivalent to a foundation of shifting sands:

And the rain descended, and the floods came,
and the winds blew, and beat upon that house;
and it fell:
and great was the fall of it.
MATTHEW 7:27

Or, your foundation could be a *person*. If that Person is the eternal Son of God, your choice of foundations is the Rock of Ages.

And the rain descended, and the floods came,
and the winds blew, and beat upon that house;
   and it fell not:
for it was founded upon a rock.

MATTHEW 7:25

With this foundation for our lives, we can join millions of others in singing this hymn, written two centuries ago:

Rock of Ages, cleft for me,
   Let me hide myself in Thee:
Let the water and the blood,
   From Thy riven side which flowed,
Be of sin the double cure,
   Cleanse me from its guilt and power.

AUGUSTUS M. TOPLADY

Many vocal and instrumental artists and speakers pay professionals to learn the art of properly walking out on the stage, bowing, standing and leaving the stage.

Many facets of thinking and interest are new with the Jet Set, but not the interest in visual poise.

"My mother never would suffer one of her children to go to a dancing school," wrote John Wesley (1703-1791), the father of Methodism. "But she had a dancing master to come to her house who taught all of us what was sufficient in her presence. To this I have no objection. If I had convenience, I would be glad to have all our preachers taught, even by a dancing-master, to make a bow and to go in and out of a room."[1]

How to Enter a Room

1. Pause in the doorway with a graceful stance.
2. Glance pleasantly around the room. It does not take long to size up a room and to find what chairs are empty. Smile at and greet some of your friends as you look around,

[1] Quoted by Rita F. Snowden in *Such a Woman* copyright 1962 by The Upper Room and used by permission.

but don't make a big production of it. You are there now,
to . . .

3. Choose a chair.

This method eliminates the ruffled appearance of one
who rushes headlong into a room and *then,* wondering
where she will sit, turns self-consciously around trying
to locate a chair. Decide on the chair that is best for your
height. If there's only one chair left, that's it . . . with a
roomful of ladies. However, if this is a mixed group, the
men would have stood by now, so you would have a
variety of chairs from which to choose.

4. Walk directly to the chair, neither rushing nor
dawdling. Maintain your good posture every step of the
way. This is one of the most important times to remember to lead with your *thighs,* because of a tendency to
lean the body way forward and to bend the knees as if
sitting, thus giving a "sitting walk" demonstration all the
way to the chair. Your walk, except for the direction you
are taking, should not even indicate that you plan to sit.

5. Sit down (see chapter 10).

A Check-List of Your Physical Walk

The store-front windows check

1. Watch the top of your *head.* Is it shooting up and
down like an erratic stock market report or does it glide
smoothly along parallel to the window frame (as if you
were on a skate-board)?

2. Are you leading with your head or with your *thighs?*

3. Does your reflection indicate that you are *"thinking
tall"* (head and chest up, back straight, abdomen and seat
in)?

4. Are your *shoulders* relaxed, or do they have that
football uniform look?

5. Are your *arms* and *legs* swinging naturally, or do they emulate a tin soldier?

6. Is your *chin* parallel to the sidewalk, or is it stretched up at a haughty angle, or down giving a defeated appearance?

7. What about your *elbows?* Don't let them wander out. They *belong* to you!

8. Now, check the reflection of your *face.* Does it look relaxed and happy? Or, perhaps, tense, worried, or bored? Regardless of how you feel, put on an assured happy face! This will be a boost to all who pass you, and will even make you feel better.

Vi always looks as if she had just received unexpected good news. Her happy expression makes others realize that perhaps things are not all black in their lives either.

Jan's sparkly, happy-go-healthy glow says, "Life is a great adventure, and I'm not about to be just an observer."

We realize that physical weaknesses or deformities could make following all the rules for good posture, walking and sitting impossible. But it's the ideal which we present. We know that each of you will do your very best.

The shadow check

1. Is the top of your head shadowing along smoothly? Even on curbs? (Flex your knees, actually *bend* them, and you will have no jerky head movements . . . just smooth . . . as you go up and down curbs.)

2. What about your posture?

3. Check the length of your arm swinging arc and of your stride.

The snow check

1. Are your footprints parallel to each other? Or are they toeing in or out?

2. How far apart are they? About the length of your foot?

The walker-watching check

Standing on a subway or train station stairway or sitting in an air, bus, or train terminal gives you a vantage view of a conglomeration of walks.

You will spot several ungainly ones which you have already demonstrated before your mirror. But concentrate on the good walkers, e.g., the stewardesses. They have been taught to walk correctly and usually are excellent examples — from a pleasant face down to parallel feet!

The television check

1. You might not be interested in the story (turn off the sound) but on occasion it would be good to turn on some dramatic presentation (even a daytime soap-box opera) just to observe how the actresses walk, stand (chapter 9) and sit (chapter 10).

She Walks in Beauty

Echoes and Overtones

She walks in beauty, like the night
 Of cloudless chimes and starry skies;
And all that's best of dark and bright
 Meet in her aspect and her eyes:
Thus mellowed to that tender light
 Which heaven to gaudy day denies.
One shade the more, one ray the less,
 Had half impaired the nameless grace
Which waves in every raven tress,
 Or softly lightens o'er her face;
Where thoughts serenely sweet express
 How pure, how dear their dwelling-place.

And on that cheek and o'er that brow,
So soft, so calm, yet eloquent,
The smiles that win, the tints that glow,
But tell of days in goodness spent,
A mind at peace with all below,
A heart whose love is innocent!

GEORGE NOEL GORDON, LORD BYRON

He that walketh with wise men shall be wise:
but a companion of fools shall be destroyed.

PROVERBS 13:20

If we walk in the light,
as he is in the light,
we have fellowship
one with another,
and the blood of Jesus Christ, his Son
cleanseth us from all sin.

I JOHN 1:7

I thought on my ways,
and turned my feet unto thy testimonies.

PSALM 119:59

As ye have therefore received Christ Jesus the Lord,
so walk ye in him:
Rooted and built up in Him,
and stablished in the faith,
as ye have been taught,
abounding therein with thanksgiving.

COLOSSIANS 2:6

12

Apples of Gold
in Pictures of Silver

The last chapter — so soon?

Our first chapter listed the three points on which others judge us: 1) the way we look, 2) the way we talk, and 3) the way we act.

Charming You has admittedly discussed only *one* of these three points — that of *the way we look*, our general appearance!

Now, as to *the way we act!*

Our day-to-day social intercourse is of tremendous importance. Our contacts with others encompass such a gamut of areas that to cover these multitudinous situations would require nothing short of a complete book — and that by a recognized authority.

In the Introduction to her *Complete Book of Etiquette*, Amy Vanderbilt writes:

> Who needs a book of etiquette? Everyone does. The simplest family . . . needs to know at least the elementary rules. Even the most sophisticated man or woman used to a great variety of social demands cannot hope to remember every single aspect

of etiquette applying to even one possible social contingency . . . .
We must all learn the socially acceptable ways of living with
others in no matter what society we move. Even in primitive
societies there are such rules, some of them as complex and
inexplicable as many of our own.[1]

In reading through several books on etiquette, I have
been impressed with the thought that basically they are
all expansions of a Biblical theme — the Golden Rule. "As
ye would that men should do to you, do you also to them
in like manner." (St. Luke 6:31, Douay Version)

This is the base, the common rule, that inspires a smile,
a kindness, an interest in others and so helps us grow "in
favor with man." But the ramifications of social intercourse demand the spelling out of its many intricacies.
Again, only a complete authoritative book on etiquette
can pinpoint these satisfactorily.

If you do not own a book of etiquette, may this not be
the opportune time for you to purchase an up-to-date
one? One prefers to have this reference book at finger-tip
rather than city-library reach, for an immediate answer
to some social amenity about which one is a little fuzzy.

A copy of: 1) the Bible, 2) an up-to-date dictionary,
and 3) a book on etiquette compose a trilogy essential to
anyone's library. They *are* a library. Without these three
books, a room boasting of thousands of books would still
be incomplete as a library. This mini-library of three
books provides a solid corner-stone for further expansion
of one's collection of books over the years.

Charming You has attempted to satisfactorily probe the
subject of "How We Look," and a complete authoritative
book on etiquette will take care of "How We Act." The

[1] From *Amy Vanderbilt's Complete Book of Etiquette*. Copyright ©
1952, 1955, 1956 and 1958 by Amy Vanderbilt. Reprinted by permission of Doubleday & Company, Inc.

third observation, "How We Talk," could also well fill a book, and has, many times. However, this chapter will hopefully offer enough pertinent ideas to be of specific help in daily conversation.

I once heard Billy Graham say that he reads daily from the book of Psalms to learn how to live with God, and from the book of Proverbs to learn how to live with people. Many of the proverbs stand out like beautiful cameos; for instance, "A word fitly spoken is like apples of gold in pictures of silver" (Proverbs 25:11, King James Version).

Doesn't this particular "cameo" portray to you maturity, thoughtfulness and intelligence in conversation? Conversation is communication which opens doors to others' lives. Through it we can tap their thoughts. Conversation is a vital exchange of minds, personalities, emotions and attitudes.

We depend upon the various transportation facilities for the movement of people and goods, and upon speech for the movement of ideas.

"A word fitly spoken is like apples of gold in pictures of silver" implies thought in choice of words, timing, and manner of delivery.

An expansion of these three aspects of conversation will conclude our book.

Choice of Words

Many homes do not possess typewriters, because there is no particular need for them. But every person in every home owns a "trite-writer." Its keys punch out *sayings* rather than single letters. It is lodged in one's brain and so is invisible, but one's conversation can quickly reveal its presence. A series of responses starts when a thought wave, prompted by a word or idea, punches a key on this "trite-writer" and the trite saying automatically rolls out through one's mouth.

To test how the "trite-writer" works, say the first word or expression which comes to your mind after each of the following:

1. As slippery as an ____.
2. Put your shoulder ____.
3. As still as a ____.
4. As fresh as a ____.
5. It's sad but ____.[2]

The fact that your responses could be predicted shows that you own a "trite-writer." This is a fact of life and nothing of which to be ashamed because a possession may be used often, seldom or practically never.

Is it not mental laziness which gives these hackneyed expressions verbal attire? Keep them in a locked vault and think up something original to say!

Think about that first expression, "as slippery as an eel." Treat your listeners to a different word picture . . . "as slippery as a freshly-oiled baby"; "as slippery as a peeled Concord grape."

Now it's your turn!

Occasional triteness is overlooked, but anyone whose conversation indicates that she is a skilled "tritist" will herself soon be overlooked. The old Greek proverb, "For that which is sweet, if it be oft repeated, is no longer sweet," would seem to hold true except in limited situations where repetition enhances sweetness, as in, "I love you!"

My husband likes to buy *Mechanix Illustrated* because of Tom McCahill's picturesque writings. For example, in describing the Lotus-Cortina, he wrote "From a looks

[2] 1. eel. 2. to the wheel. 3. mouse. 4. daisy. 5. true.

standpoint the Cortina is like seeing Hoss Cartwright modeling a negligee at a fashion show."

Rhoda, a clever childhood friend of mine, once chose "garbage, rubbish, and ashes" for her slang expression of the moment. Unmitigated plagiarism from her civics textbook . . . but refreshingly novel!

The following slang expressions are new to no one, they show no thought or originality, and contribute nothing but sustained boredom to any conversation:

> You can say that again!
> That's for sure!
> It's out of this world!
> It's great!
> It's terrific!
> It's fantastic!

Why not substitute some vivid word pictures — hilarious, superb, worthwhile, relaxing, meticulous, stimulating, awe-inspiring, beautiful, scintillating!

Uncomplimentary comments can be equally trite:

> It's stupid.
> It's rotten.
> It's lousy.

What one really means is probably — irritating, innocuous, time-wasting, unpleasant, incoherent, offensive, dull, inappropriate, monotonous, crude, or boring!

Reading helps equip one to speak intelligently and to dress his thoughts with precise word pictures.

Limiting one's vocabulary to a few nondescript words is like a child automatically ordering a hamburger while disregarding the menu card with its generous array of mouth-watering entrees.

Please read this lazily told incident:

"I got up earlier than usual this a.m. because I got a

telephone call which I didn't expect to get until later. My sister had just got into town and couldn't get a taxi so she called me to come get her. I got to the airport in about fifteen minutes. I would have got there in about ten minutes, except that I got caught in a traffic jam.

"It was wonderful to get to see my sister again. We got our breakfast at the airport restaurant and got a sweeping view of the airport from our table. We got caught up on the family news. We got out of there after getting our check, and got home about 10:00 a.m."

"Get" it?

Underline the original verb in that story and its fifteen repetitions, and in each instance, where a verb is needed, try substituting one which is more expressive to that particular thought.

Isn't it a treat to listen to one who edits his own conversation and who has a workable vocabulary from which to draw clearly defined word pictures? Such a person compliments his listener as one who is important enough to *think* for.

There is the anecdote of a serviceman who showered and put on his best clothes before calling his girl friend long distance.

People are important!

Do you agree that the efforts we put into our appearance and into our conversation parallel the amount of respect we have for *others* and for *ourselves?*

Girls over the years have been advised by their mothers, "Talk like a lady — not necessarily because the one to whom you are speaking is a lady, but because *you* are!"

Regardless of your age, continue to build your vocabulary. This does not mean to try to sound impressive by using multi-syllabled words. Rather, it means that as the owner of a Word Storehouse, with neatly laden shelves, you will be able to take your pick of articulate, appropriate words. Refuse to be identified as one whose thoughts are painfully dragged out through an unappetizing mixture of "Ah-er-um's," tritisms, and ineffective words.

Calvin Coolidge, never accused of being loquacious, is supposed to have been asked by a farmer concerning a certain politician, "How long has he been talking?"

"An hour and a half," was the reply.

"What's he talking about?" queried the farmer.

"He doesn't say," droned Coolidge.

Timing in Conversation

You have been warned from early childhood against interrupting someone else's conversation. But don't you consider inattention (eyes wandering, a bored yawn) or an obvious anxiety to interrupt talk, equally rude?

A good conversationalist has the ability to draw others into conversation, rather than giving a monologue of his own activities or thoughts.

True conversation grows and blossoms before one's eyes, like a tight bud opening in time-lapse photography into a full-bloomed Peace Rose around which a butterfly is hovering.

Conversation is the sharing of ideas of thinking people who wish to learn from others as well as to express themselves. It is talking and it is listening.

Conversational listening doesn't mean waiting impatiently for the end of someone else's thoughts so that you can inject some little nugget stored up to outdo or squelch what has been said. It means truly listening to another's ideas. It is looking at that person while you try to think his thoughts with him.

Give of yourself to others. Give your ideas and your attention.

Don't underestimate the importance of listening! A good listener is an active partner, providing a sounding board, like the garage door to someone practicing returning tennis balls. But as a conversationalist, you will want, at times, to metamorphize from a garage door into a partner who actively returns the ball.

Gauge your rate of speaking by the speed with which your listener absorbs your ideas. Consider the other person's point of view. Communicate. Talk a sentence. Talk a paragraph. Pauses are important and should come at the right places. Study your listener's face for reactions.

Be natural in your talking and in your listening. Forced attention or a taut, self-conscious voice puts a strain on any conversation.

Take time out now to think of all your acquaintances who put you at ease. What is it about these people, from different age brackets and with divergent interests, which makes you feel relaxed and comfortable? Isn't it that their looks and actions indicate that they really like you and accept you the way you are? I think so!

If, while you are talking, your partner's expression were to indicate "How can you be so dull?" or "You're so naive . . . desperately lacking in social graces!" or, "Why don't you do something with your hair?" you would be made uncomfortable and being on the defensive would become an even duller conversational partner.

Listen in conversation! Listen with open, attentive eyes and with open attentive ears. *Listen as you would be listened to.*

"To everything there is a season, and a time to every

purpose under the heaven: . . . a time to keep silence, and a time to speak" (Ecclesiastes 3:1, 7).

Communicate with your friends. Share their joys and their sorrows at the time when this would be most appreciated. Don't procrastinate until the original significance has become lukewarm or faded.

Before leaving this aspect of conversation, let's remind ourselves of that basic rule of life, "As you would that men should do to you, do you also to them in like manner."

Manner of Delivery

Your two newly respected allies, 1) Sparkling Appearance and 2) Visual Poise, assure a beautiful picture of you. We could wish that picture were spot-proof. But it isn't, any more than that array of bleached white clothes hanging in the sunshine. Don't let a poor voice be the pigeon which stains your attractive picture!

What you say and the way in which you say it shows the kind of person you really are. Your speech reveals your intelligence, your background, your charm, and your consideration for others. Your voice has the power to attract or to repel others. Every day you are heard by many people — the members of your family, your friends, people at school, business or social gatherings. Treat these people to a pleasant, well-modulated voice which shows respect for the listener and for yourself. Check your diction and your grammar.

When you talk you are actually asking for the floor, for a person's time, and for his attention. Therefore you should speak as if what you are saying is worth something. No one can evaluate your ideas (either to accept or to reject them) if they are given as a hodgepodge.

Maintain eye contact as you converse.

Organize what you are saying so that it will be lucid.
Do not be a question mark dispenser, leaving a question
mark hanging above each of your listener's heads.

Oral wandering and repetitions are hardly stimulating
fare.

The pitch of your voice

The pitch of your voice is important in helping your
meanings to be understood. Hum *your* speaking tone, the
tone most natural for you. Find it on the piano. Now,
when you want to emphasize a word, pitch it five notes
above your regular tone (less than this will not be em-
phatic enough). If you have no piano, just call your tone,
"do," and sing "do . . . mi . . . sol." This "sol" would be
a fifth above your natural tone.

One sentence can demonstrate the importance of striking a higher note to emphasize a word. Read the following sentence aloud five times, emphasizing a different word
each time:

I think I'll go to the play tonight.

1. Emphasize "I" and it implies that someone else does
not think you will.

2. Emphasize "think" and it shows uncertainty on your
own part.

3. Emphasizing "I'll" implies, "even if you don't."

4. Emphasizing "play" would indicate that there is a
choice of activities going on tonight.

5. Raising your voice on "tonight" suggests at least a
two-night running of the play.

The general rule is for the voice to come *down* at the
end of a sentence (exceptions would be: 1) all questions
and 2) a sentence like #5 above).

There is no one ideal voice for all to copy. Strive to

have your voice represent the best by having it warm, friendly, sympathic, and mature. Your voice should reinforce the picture of yourself which you want others to have.

"The words are right but the music all wrong," was succinctly put by Mark Twain. Reinforce your words with appropriate tone and pitch. Make them sound as if you have thought them out and actually mean to say them.

The quality of a voice betrays specific personality characteristics. As you wander throughout a large department store, you can detect a wide variety of voices: enthusiastic, dogmatic, warm, complaining, cultured, whining, immature, and sympathetic.

The emphasis one uses in talking is important. Remember to time your words and to be aware of pitch. Be self-assured and *sound* it! Respect your own ideas. Others cannot be expected to think highly of you unless you do yourself!

Place your fingers at the end of your jaws, just under your ears. Now, as you open and close your mouth, you will realize that it is only the lower jaw which is moving, and you will be able to feel the hinge which attaches it to the upper jaw.

Your upper jaw is not expected to move, but the *lower* one *is*. Unless you're a ventriloquist, you have no excuse for being either lazy-jawed, or lazy-lipped. No, your jaw won't drop as you say, "e," but if it doesn't drop on "yah," you are lazy-jawed.

Look in the mirror. Move your jaw as you talk. Actually shape your words with your lips, rather than just barely moving your lips.

The best mirror for your speaking voice is a tape recorder. Warning . . . it will be a shock to hear your voice for the first time! It isn't uncommon to hear a startled "Do I really sound like that?" "How can people stand me?" "That can't be me, I mean 'I' . . . Whatever I mean, it just can't *be!*"

You have no tape recorder? The next best thing is to cup your hands behind your ears, pushing your ears forward and then read aloud. This will sound to you very much as you sound to others.

The sound of your voice

1. *How is your overall speech sound?* It could be masculine (pitched too low), childish (pitched too high), hoarse, harsh, soft, pleasant, nasal (as with a clothespin on one's nose).

Actually the only sounds which are truly nasal are *m, n,* and *ng.*

To check yourself as to whether or not you speak with a nasal tone, pinch your nose and spell *meandering* aloud. You should feel nasal vibrations on the *m* and the two *n*'s, but not on any other letters.

Now, pronounce *me-an-der-ing* aloud. All of the syllables except the third should sound nasal or fuzzy. If *-der* is not clear, then you do have a nasal tone. Continue to speak or read aloud (with your nose pinched) until all syllables (except those with *m, n,* and *ng)* come through clearly, with no fuzziness.

Ladies, your voices sound warmer, more pleasant and more mature in the *lower register.* Keep them down.

2. What about *your rate of speech?* Do you speak too fast, making it difficult for your listeners to catch their breath?

Do you speak too slowly, causing your listeners to fidget while they wish they could reel in the line faster for you?

Do you speak jerkily? This lack of rhythm, if carried to extremes, can be most annoying and unsettling to a listener.

Aim for a speaking speed that is comfortable to listen to.

3. How about *the resonance of your voice?* Is your voice flat and dull, or can you hear a resonance (natural music) in it?

"How wonderful is the human voice! It is indeed the organ of the soul," said Longfellow.

As one talks, the air comes up from the lungs through the trachea and starts the vibration of the larynx (voice box). As you move your tongue over the roof of your mouth, the hard part you feel is the hard palate, and the part behind that, the soft palate. The latter moves with every sound you make. Your teeth also, play an important part in speech, as evidenced by the speech of a little child or an adult who is missing one or more teeth.

When you are nervous or cross, your vocal chords become tense and your voice sounds thinner and more highly pitched. This is more noticeable and objectionable in women's voices than in men's. When your vocal chords are relaxed, you speak naturally and the resulting sound is pleasant.

Your diaphragm, the horizontal muscle separating your chest and abdominal cavities, is the control, the basis for good speaking and singing. Proper use of the diaphragm will give your voice more depth and better quality because shallow breathing will be replaced with deep breathing.

Place your hand on your diaphragm and say, "ha, ha, ha." If your hand isn't moving, you're not using your diaphragm. Now, try it again, until the action of your diaphragm moves your hand. That's better!

Keeping your hand on your diaphragm, and continuing

to breathe deeply, please sing the following exercise, emphasizing diaphragmatic movement on each syllable of the last line.

Laugh-ing is con-ta-gious,
(do, mi, sol, fa, mi, re)
And it's ad-van-ta-geous,
(do, mi, sol, fa, mi, re)
Ha, ha, ha, ha, ha, ha, ha!
(do, mi, sol, fa, mi, re, do)

Repeat this exercise, substituting in turn, 1) *he,* 2) *ho,* and 3) *who* for *ha.* Continue to emphasize diaphragmatic movement.

Mother passed this exercise on to us from her vocal teacher, the late Daniel B. Towner (1850-1919) of Chicago. You will find his name as the composer of such famous familiar hymn tunes as "Trust and Obey," "Nor Silver Nor Gold," "Grace Greater Than Our Sin," "At Calvary," "My Anchor Holds," and "Anywhere With Jesus."

Dr. Towner had his pupils start this exercise with *do* at middle C, the next time with *do* at D, and so on up the scale, as high as they could sing, changing keys each time.

4. *With how much clarity do you speak?* Are your sounds muffled (like speaking with a hot potato in your mouth)?

Are your words run together?

Jever? (Did you ever?)
Jeet jet? (Did you eat yet?)
Nojew? (No. Did you?)

Or do you speak articulately?

5. *What is your A.Q.* (alertness quotient)? Does your voice sound sleepy, dull, monotonous, bored, or alert?

Your telephone is ringing!

As soon as you answer it, your voice will start painting a picture of you. What will it represent?

Come, stroll with me past an imaginary art display, where all the pictures inspired by varied telephone voices depict what these voices indicate.

(1.) A harried housewife (with two children contemplating mayhem, and a blueberry pie bubbling over in the oven).

(2.) An efficient organizer (the computer type, saying, "1, 2, 3 . . . Answer").

(3.) A self-centered, honey-voiced coquette.

(4.) A bored girl from Dullsville.

(5.) A super-charged salesgirl (with bulging eyes and flushed cheeks).

(6.) Little Miss Shallow (operating her "trite-writer").

(7.) A brusque, no-time-for-details gal.

(8.) A chatty little Miss Loquacious (with tongue wagging at both ends).

(9.) A ravenous teenager attempting to talk while devouring a hamburger and a double-malted.

(10.) A pleasing picture of a warm, polite, intelligent lady.

Talk directly into the mouth-piece of your telephone, with your lips about one-half inch away from it.

"Let your speech be always in grace seasoned with salt; that you may know how you ought to answer every man" (Colossians 4:6, Douay version).

A salt shaker next to the telephone could silently remind us that it is salt *(not pepper)* with which we are to season our speech. I find that pepper shakes out more naturally on those friendly, intimate-sounding "pals" who turn out

to be telephone salesmen (especially if their persistent ringing has called me from the family dinner table or the
bathtub).

One gimmick to help resist "pouring on the pepper" is
to picture your caller in a wheel chair. It could be that he
is *not* just a lazy salesman, with both feet propped up on a
desk while one hand fingers an opened telephone directory.

Another telephone nicety is to rub or spray some perfume on the mouthpiece. This olfactory treat for yourself
should, by suggestion, help "sweeten" your conversation.

Make a practice of reading aloud each day. Read poetry,
the Bible, hymns, magazine articles, the newspaper, even
advertisements (if nothing else is available at the moment).
Any thoughtful oral practice is beneficial.

You have no one to whom to read? Be your own daily
listener.

And, on occasion, let your reading add a bright dimension to someone else's life . . . perhaps a resident at a nurs-
ing or retirement home. This service should boomerang
to help you, too, by adding an extra warmth and sparkle
to your "apples of gold in pictures of silver."

Apples of Gold in Pictures of Silver

Echoes and Overtones

Speak gently! 'tis a little thing
  Dropped in the heart's deep well;
The good, the joy that it may bring
  Eternity shall tell.
                    G. W. Langford

Good manners are made up of petty sacrifices.
                    Ralph Waldo Emerson

Let the words of my mouth,
    and the meditation of my heart,
be acceptable in thy sight,
    O Lord, my strength, and my redeemer.
                    Psalm 19:14

A Morning Prayer
Keep me, O God, from every evil word —
From worry, fear, idleness, hasty temper,
Useless complaint and falsehood.
Make my heart pure and my lips clean.
Give me to share thy joys
And let my words and deeds
Be full of courage and good cheer,
Lest I should bear false witness to thy loving care.
Give me strength sufficient for this day's duties
And enough besides to keep me kind.
                    Author Unknown

My Prayer

Give me a good digestion, Lord,
And also something to digest.
Give me a healthy mind, O Lord,
To keep the good and pure in sight,
Which seeing sin is not appalled
But finds a way to set it right.
Give me a mind that is not bound
That does not whimper, whine or sigh
Don't let me worry over much
About this funny thing called I.
Give me a sense of humor, Lord,
And sense enough to see a joke,
To get more happiness out of life
And pass it on to other folk.

ANONYMOUS
Chester Cathedral, England

And Now, Good-By, Girls!

May the road rise to meet you,
May the wind be always at your back,
May the sun shine warm upon your face,
And the rains fall soft upon your fields,
And until we meet again,
May God hold you in the palm of His Hand.

AN OLD GAELIC BLESSING